W9-CZO-655

THE
ARIADNE CLUE

THE
ARIADNE CLUE

 Carol Clemeau

CHARLES SCRIBNER'S SONS · NEW YORK

NOV 1 '82

Copyright © 1982 Carol Clemeau

Library of Congress Cataloging in Publication Data

Clemeau, Carol.
  The Ariadne clue.
  I. Title.
PS3553.L392A89 1982   813'.54   82–10359
ISBN 0–684–17764–1

1 3 5 7 9 11 13 15 17 19 F/C 20 18 16 14 12 10 8 6 4 2

Printed in the United States of America.

To my Father and Mother

Contents

In Greek legend, the Cretan king Minos offended the god of the sea by refusing to sacrifice to him a beautiful white bull. In revenge the god caused Minos' queen, Pasiphaë, to fall in love with the bull and conceive by it a monstrous offspring called the Minotaur. The half-human creature was imprisoned in a maze called the Labyrinth, where it fed upon youths and maidens that Minos forced his subject city Athens to supply.

The Athenian prince Theseus appeared one day at Minos' palace and quickly won the heart of the king's elder daughter, Ariadne. The princess gave him a ball of thread, or clew, which he was to tie to the doorpost of the Labyrinth when he entered and unwind behind him as he went in search of the Minotaur in its depths. After slaying the monster, he could retrace his steps to the entrance with the help of the thread.

The scheme worked: the hero emerged victorious from the Labyrinth, carried off the princess who had saved his life and enhanced his reputation, and sailed away into the Aegean sunset. Unfortunately, however, he abandoned Ariadne halfway back to Athens; the legend says he "forgot" her.

Although Ariadne's fate after Theseus left her is variously described, all versions agree that her younger sister, Phaedra, later married the ungrateful prince, to his bitter sorrow. But that is another story.

1

Now that April's Here

WHY HAD SHE SAID NO?

She stared unseeing at the manicured expanses of green—a green, at this time of year, so implausible as to suggest Astroturf rather than living grass—and saw instead the lush greens of the Mesara in April, green of lemon and orange groves and wild grasses starred with white flowers.

Why *had* she said no?

She heard the slap of her own sandals on the poured-concrete walkways that crisscrossed the campus and remembered the smell of hot stone above Kato Zakro. Living too, that stone—alive with the pungency of thyme and the upbeating heat of a Cretan summer.

Why on *earth* had she said no?

She stopped abstractedly at one of the chrome and fiberglass kiosks that announced "Coming Events of Interest to the University Community." The poster for the Aegean Gold exhibition was simple but effective: the famous Mask of Agamemnon on a black ground, and below it in simple black letters on a wide band of gold, the words AEGEAN GOLD. *University Museum. April 15– June 3.* That was all, but such was the genius of the nameless Mycenean artist that no more was needed to compel the attention of

1

the passerby. Golden eyelids closed in death, lean golden aristocratic nose, thin severe lips of gold—perhaps, thought Antonia, it was the tension between the austerity of that ancient face and the barbaric splendor of the material that gave the thing such power.

Reluctantly, Antonia tore her attention away from the poster and looked around as if to remind herself where she was.

She was a couple of hundred yards from her destination, the Humanities Building. She was surrounded by the artificially gentled slopes of an urban university campus on the East Coast, by clouds of dogwood and great spraying fountains of forsythia, by carpets of crocus and violets. The temperature, quite remarkably for early April, was already well into the seventies even though it was only eight-thirty.

Perhaps it wasn't too late even now to say yes.

It was almost two months since the girl had invited Antonia to spend the summer with her in Crete, among her uncountable uncles and cousins and great-aunts. The invitation was awkward and abrupt, as lacking in social grace as Ariadne herself and as fiercely sincere.

"I thought," the girl said gruffly, "we could hike around from village to village—they're scattered all over the island, my people. Can't afford anything else, and they wouldn't mind putting you up too. If you're interested."

Antonia had hesitated, searching for words that would express both the firm refusal that was necessary and warm appreciation, words that would be something more than polite clichés. Ariadne was not a person to be dismissed with a cliché.

But as Antonia groped for the right phrase, the girl spoke again. "Phaistos," she said, "and Ayia Triadha. Gournia. Zakro." Her voice, no longer gruff with shyness, caressed the harsh old names as if they were the names of lovers. Yet Antonia knew Ariadne had never seen the palaces and shops and country houses of Minoan Crete, except in her imagination and in books.

"And Knossos, of course." Here the young voice had seemed to falter momentarily, but it grew strong and resonant again as she concluded, "It might be kind of a *different* way of seeing the island, for you I mean. For me it's the *only* way—the only way I can afford."

Antonia had declined, of course. The litany of ancient Minoan sites kindled her imagination almost as much as it did Ariadne's. The prospect of spending the summer in a series of Greek farmhouses, far from putting her off, as the girl seemed to fear, was a powerful inducement. Even the prospect of tramping the baked hillsides and subtropical plains of Crete in July didn't deter her. She had done it once, as a graduate student, and she could do it again.

She had declined, quite simply, because she didn't believe in close teacher–student friendships, neither in their desirability nor even in their possibility.

But now—two months later and less than three weeks from the end of the spring semester—she was less certain.

In those two months, her odd relationship with the Greek girl had changed subtly. The distance that Antonia had always maintained between herself and her students remained. Neither called the other by her first name; they never saw each other except in Antonia's office. Their talk was exclusively of what Antonia's colleagues would have called "professional matters."

Yet their conversations, Antonia thought wryly, would hardly have passed muster as "professional" in some quarters. They had never so much as alluded to the academic job market, the latest issue of the *American Journal of Philology,* or the contacts they had made or failed to make at last December's American Philological Association convention. Oddest of all, they had never once talked about Ariadne's dissertation. The girl herself never brought the matter up, and Antonia steered clear of it, thinking that perhaps it was taboo, graduate students being notoriously touchy on the subject of half-finished doctoral theses.

But they had discussed the tangled question of Euripides' attitude toward women, the curious mixture of sympathy and horror with which he portrays his terrible heroines. Once Ariadne had put forth a strikingly original interpretation of the *Iliad* that had so impressed Antonia that she urged her to think seriously about working it up and publishing. Astoundingly, Ariadne had only shrugged. Once they had talked of Michael Ventris' decipherment of the Mycenean–Minoan syllabary in the fifties, and of the electrifying moment when the young Englishman announced to the world of scholarship, "The language is Greek!" Characteristically, Ariadne's dark eyes had shone with excitement as she repeated in a whisper, " '*The language is Greek!*' Those were my people, Miss Nielsen, and until Ventris we weren't even sure they were Greek!" You might have thought someone had accused her ancestors of having tails or being ignorant of fire and language.

Yes, passionate intensity and a profoundly personal involvement with her subject were very definitely Ariadne's mode. No doubt the approach had its limitations. It wouldn't always be easy for her to maintain either tolerance or the scholarly "objectivity" so dear to the academic heart. But by God she was refreshing after the cold-blooded careerists and intellectual file clerks who littered the groves of academe nowadays.

From these few conversations with Ariadne, conversations unrelieved by anything so social as even a cup of coffee, Antonia had had more "intellectual stimulation" (as her colleagues would, without enthusiasm, have called it) than from five years of desultory chatting around the coffee urn in the faculty lounge.

An unconventional relationship. And yet it was on grounds of convention, of what was not or should not be done, that she had rejected the girl's invitation. Was she perhaps becoming as careful, as conventional, as fearful of even the pettiest risks as her colleagues, as her students, for that matter? And what on earth would she be risking anyway? Convention no longer militated against student–faculty relationships of any kind at all, let alone one as devoid of sexual overtones as hers and Ariadne's. No, the barrier was strictly of her own erecting, based on a vague feeling that there would be less trouble, less friction, less confusion of roles if she kept her distance from her students, all her students.

But now, as she looked around her once more at the neat, artfully landscaped campus, Antonia was struck by its resemblance to the lives of its denizens. Attractive, intelligently planned, without violent contrasts or inconsistencies, it was a landscape in which change was permitted only in the form of long gentle dips and rises duly graded and turfed and mowed, a landscape without crags and without chasms.

She thought again of the summer five years ago when she had hiked through Crete, of the eye-searing glare of whitewashed walls against cerulean sea, the rugged limestone gorges and precipices of the south, the crushing heat of the wind that comes in from Libya. Violent, unmodulated, uncompromising country—and suddenly she felt all the pettiness and timidity of her refusal to go there with Ariadne.

Moreover, there were no emotional encumbrances at the moment. There had been a man, but both he and the brief regret that lingered after him were gone now, leaving behind only the pleasant sense that she was absolutely free to do as she liked—to go to Crete with Ariadne, for instance.

It was what she wanted, it was what she would do, and she would tell Ariadne at twelve-thirty.

Spring fever, with Antonia, often took the form of wanderlust. She had never been really comfortable with the enforced immobility of the academic year, short though it was. But her restlessness always became particularly acute at just about this point in second semester: three more weeks of classes, exams and grading for another two weeks after that, and through it all morale—hers and everyone else's—at low ebb.

But now that something had been decided, now that there was a definite terminus to her presence on campus— what had Ariadne said? May twentieth, something like that —the flowery blandness of the place didn't seem nearly so depressing.

Not only were leaves and grass showing signs of awakening; even the students seemed to have taken a new lease on life, at least temporarily, until exams began and term papers fell due. Young shoulders were held a little straighter under the green khaki straps of book bags, and there was a jaunty swing to the long coltish legs instead of the despairing trudge of recent months. Frisbees, as well as birdsong, were in the air: one of them sliced across Antonia's path just east of Everett Hall, narrowly missing her nose. A few hours hence, if the thermometer continued its present trend, large numbers of luscious young bodies would be draped in various degrees of near nudity over every available square yard of grass on campus.

The one incongruous element in this idyllic scene was the media people. Even before the warm spell, Antonia had noticed an occasional photographer lugging equipment up the steps of the museum or crouching in odd corners to get dramatic angle shots of its façade. But now, only eight days before the much-publicized opening of the Aegean Gold exhibition, the photographers were everywhere. One of them, a shaggy youth in jeans, waylaid Antonia herself as she rounded the corner of the Humanities Building. She was passing between him and an Aegean Gold poster tacked to the trunk of a maple tree, and his idea seemed to be to catch the poster, the tree's bark, Antonia's emerald-green dress, and a chunk of abnormally blue sky in a single off-beat composition. This she deduced from the fact that he was lying on the grass, awkwardly supported on his left hip and elbow, squinting up at her through his lens. She obliged by gazing for a moment at the poster with what she hoped was the proper professorial intentness, then flashed him a thoroughly unprofessorial grin and continued on her way.

"Dynamite shot, Miss!" he called after her. "Thanks a lot!" Antonia waved back at him without turning around.

As she started up the steps of the Humanities Building, a stocky figure erupted from the main entrance and plunged down the steps, almost colliding with her. It was Tommy Wakowski, one of the Classics graduate students, and he was probably due at a class on the opposite side of campus in three minutes. He usually was.

"Oh, hi, Miss Nielsen," he panted. "Sorry if I—say, do you happen to know where I could find Ariadne? I need to borrow her Teubner Bacchylides."

"Sorry, Tommy, I don't know where she is right now. She has an appointment with me at twelve-thirty, though. I'll tell her you're looking for her."

"Thanks, Miss Nielsen. She sure is hard to find sometimes, Ariadne. Well, see ya." And he resumed his headlong flight across campus, careening off several fellow students who had the poor judgment to cross his path.

Antonia entered the building. The atmosphere was already stuffy; by noon it would be intolerable, especially in the tiny airless faculty offices. She headed toward hers with the pleasant sense that she was within two classes and one appointment of a spring weekend. Let Buildings and Grounds do their worst: Professor Nielsen would be sunbathing on her balcony this afternoon, thank you, sublimely indifferent to the temperature inside the Humanities Building.

And after that, a shopping expedition for something to wear to the Aegean Gold opening. Something long and fluid and white to set off the new tan that by then should be coming along nicely.

And after *that*, the Randolphs' dinner party. There would be Gillian, of course. But there was no point in speculating about the potential for trouble from that quarter. One dealt with Gillian when and as necessary, not according to some premeditated strategy that would almost certainly turn out to be irrelevant or worse. Forget her, in short, until the time came.

That still left all of Saturday and most of Sunday to work on the article she had hoped to send off to *The Classical Journal* no later than January. The demands of her job had, as usual, made it nearly impossible to find time for writing. But slowly the pages had accumulated, and now the work was tantalizingly close to completion. What remained to do was mostly fun, and she was looking forward to it.

She would talk to Ariadne after her last class, tell her she wanted to go to Crete with her after all. They would spend a delightful half hour making plans for the trip, maybe even call the travel agency and get it started on Antonia's tickets.

All in all a full, well-balanced, thoroughly satisfying weekend.

It would be two hours, almost to the minute, before it all began to fall apart.

❧2❧

The Boots of Miss Lilly

HER NINE AND TEN O'CLOCK CLASSES—THE END OF Antonia's teaching week—prolonged her sense that life was flowing along pretty much as usual. In Greek Drama in Translation she lectured on the discovery of the *Dyskolos* papyrus in 1957. Her students, predictably, were excited by the resurrection of a comedy two thousand years old and bored by the play's text. Her advanced Greek class, equally predictably, was sluggish. It is difficult at the best of times to get emotionally involved with the aorist subjunctive, nor is Thucydides commonly an undergraduate's favorite author. And when to the difficulties of morphology, syntax, and content are added the enticements of a gorgeous spring day, the first of the year—suffice it to say that Greek 406 that Friday morning was not one of Antonia's most memorable pedagogical experiences.

It was therefore with a business-as-usual sort of feeling, neither especially high nor especially low, that Antonia headed for the lounge after her last class.

The faculty lounge on the second floor of the Humanities Building, at 10:55 on a Friday morning, was always well patronized. Professors who still had one or more classes to teach would stop to refill their coffee mugs on their way to eleven o'clocks, while those who were through for the day were beginning to drift in to confirm their sense that the weekend had indeed arrived at last.

On this particular Friday, however, the lounge was doing an unusually brisk business. Small clusters of professors and teaching assistants spilled out into the hall, some waiting to get in and some, steaming mugs in hand, moving unhurriedly on an outward-bound course. The crowd was denser, the conversation noticeably less desultory than usual, though it was some time before Antonia was able to make out the cause of the excitement.

The only concrete indication that anything out of the ordinary was going on was the unwonted presence of Miss Lilly. The Humanities Building was on the opposite side of campus from her customary haunts, but there she sat, enthroned upon the less disreputable of the lounge's two sofas, surrounded by senior faculty and one or two of the more enterprising T.A.'s. It became clear to Antonia, as she made her tortuous way through the crowd toward the coffee urn, that Miss Lilly was somehow the center of the excitement.

Emma Lilly was, almost literally, a landmark on campus. During freshman orientation tours she was regularly pointed out to bewildered newcomers as one of the sights worth noting. ("On your left is Everett Hall, the last of the original buildings. Over there is Armistead Quad, where May Day festivities are held. And *that* is Miss Lilly.") She had been at the university longer than many of the buildings and before half the faculty was born.

Her impending retirement, at the end of the current semester, was viewed with regret throughout the university. In her own fiefdom, the University Museum, it was regarded as a major catastrophe. Various schemes had been put forward, only half in jest, for circumventing the retirement regulations. They ranged from petitioning for a special dispensation from the governor to falsifying Miss Lilly's birth certificate.

The mood behind these proposals, a mood that in some instances bordered on panic, was based upon the simple fact that Miss Lilly knew more about the history, the administration, and the contents of the University Museum than any oth living individual. Her official title might be assistant   .ne director, but in practice she combined the funct   of *genius loci*, data-retrieval system, and platoon se   .t.

Peering over the shoulders of the colleagues who crowded around her, Antonia thought Miss Lilly was looking a little haggard, but it was hard to be sure at such a distance. For the moment she concentrated on reaching the coffee urn.

"What *is* going on around here?" she said to the backs of the last two men standing between her and the coffee.

The two men turned to her in unison.

"You have not heard the news of Mademoiselle Lilly?" inquired Gatineau of Romance Languages.

"It's simply incredible, Antonia!" exclaimed Atwood of English.

"*Nil admirari*," said Antonia. "May I *please* have a cup of coffee before I faint at your feet?"

Atwood appropriated her mug and began to fill it from the urn while Gatineau explained, gesticulating gracefully with a slice of coffee cake.

"It is the museum, *chère collègue*. It has been—how does one say these days—torn off? The Aegean Gold has been . . ."

"Torn—you mean stolen?" she gasped. "But that's impossible."

"Afraid not," said Atwood, handing back her mug.

"Not the entire collection, of course, but some pretty choice pieces, I gather."

"One says," Gatineau added with a flourish of coffee cake, "that the chancellor is telephoning to some Greek government official in Athens at this very moment. I should not," he added with feeling, "like to be in the boots of the chancellor just now."

Nor the boots of poor Miss Lilly, for that matter, thought Antonia. She moved away from Gatineau and Atwood with a vague smile, instinctively searching for someone in her own department, someone who might feel as she did about the loss of such a treasure. But there was not a classicist anywhere in sight, except for Win Randolph on the far fringes of the crowd, and he seemed to be about to leave. There was no hope of reaching him, but she caught his eye and he smiled at her—rather wanly, she thought—but then disappeared from her view.

She decided to try Miss Lilly, who could be counted upon to have a more accurate view of the facts of the case than anyone else in the room. But approaching Miss Lilly was no simple matter, surrounded as she was by a close-packed throng, all talking at once and none of them inclined to yield his hard-won vantage point to Antonia.

She persevered, insinuating herself into the crevices that occasionally opened between two earnestly discoursing colleagues, her coffee sloshing precariously in its mug. Snatches of conversation assailed her ears from every side.

Morrisroe of Art History was saying, "There's a good deal of popular appeal in this sort of exhibition, of course —what I call the King Tut mentality—but the really *significant* thing . . ."

A short dark teaching assistant who kept running his fingers self-consciously through his hair was holding forth to an admiring circle: ". . . right there the day they uncrated. I was supposed to be helping with inventory in the storeroom, but that stuff pulled me in like a magnet. Looked like Fort Knox around there for a while—crowns and goblets and necklaces and these teacup-like things—wow! That little guy from the National Museum in Athens was hopping around like a cricket for fear we'd put a dent in his Precious. And the director, well, he was playing it cool and suave as usual, but you could tell that stuff was blowing his mind too. I mean it was like . . ."

It was a relief to come upon Win Randolph, closer now, making, like herself, slow progress toward Miss Lilly's sofa. Apparently he had not left the lounge as Antonia had supposed; he had plunged into the crowd as she had, but from the opposite side of the room.

"Well, well, Antonia, what do you make of our little mystery? Isn't often we get such a brouhaha around here before lunchtime, eh?" He grasped her elbow protectively. It was typical of Win to offer superfluous guidance to women who hadn't asked for it.

Win Randolph was a young looking forty-two with a carefully maintained physique and an elegantly flaring moustache that reminded some coeds of Faulkner and others of their fathers. He did not discourage either reaction. Though he was not tall, his body was compact and well proportioned and did full justice to the professorial tweeds and corduroys he affected. Antonia sometimes wondered, in fact, if the popular-professor persona was conscious or unconscious with him. It was so complete as to constitute almost a parody of itself, right down to the suede elbow patches and the painstakingly mellowed pipe. At any rate, whether contrived or not, the pose worked—worked, that is, if what you were after was popularity with your students.

And with your colleagues for that matter, she added to herself with scrupulous fairness. He *was* well liked among the faculty. And there had even been a time when she herself—well, thank heaven *that* had come to nothing, anyway. He had simply been extremely kind to her when she first arrived at the university five years ago, fresh out of graduate school and slightly bewildered at the prospect of her first job, had helped her find an apartment and a used car, had shoved her office furniture around until the arrangement pleased her, had introduced her to a lot of her new colleagues outside the department. He had, in short, immeasurably eased for her the passage from graduate student to professor. It would have taken longer and been more painful without him, and Antonia had been—still was—grateful.

She was slightly less grateful for his present assistance. Together they were making even slower progress through the crowd than Antonia could have made alone. And Win's excited chatter about the burglary was more irritating than enlightening.

". . . business about the Shaft Grave daggers, old girl?" he was saying.

"Good Lord!" she exclaimed, "are *they* gone?" She must have put more force into the words than she realized, because all around her the talking stopped for an instant and a dozen heads turned to stare at her. She grinned apologetically but took advantage of the slight disarrangement in the solid phalanxes around her to forge ahead once more in the direction of Miss Lilly's sofa.

Few ancient artifacts had more of what Morrisroe of Art History had just contemptuously dismissed as "popular appeal" than the famous Shaft Grave daggers, the exquisite inlaid blades that lay for thirty-four centuries in the tombs of the lords of Mycenae: golden lions and hunting leopards, silver waterfowl and tiny huntsmen with figure-eight shields —all the motifs dearest to the hearts of the Bronze Age warrior-barons, picked out in enamel and precious metals. Antonia had always had a particular fondness for these beautiful little blades, their points and cutting edges gnawed away by time and oxidation but their inlaid blades as fresh as the day they were put to rest for all eternity with the forefathers of Agamemnon.

Then suddenly, before Win could reply to Antonia's stunned question, someone stepped aside and she was standing in front of Miss Lilly.

Miss Lilly appeared to be in, or to have recently recovered from, a state of shock. Several hairs in the white chignon were actually out of place, and there was a barely perceptible tremor in the hand that held the coffee cup. But her voice, though it sounded tired, was calm and steady.

"No, my dear," she was saying to a girl Antonia recognized as one of the English department's T.A.'s, "I'm afraid it wasn't a bit like *Topkapi*. Our arrangements, I regret to say, are rather primitive. No invisible-light screens or ultrasonic waves or anything like that. I've been begging the board for a more up-to-date security system for years, but of course they're very expensive and I got nowhere. Now that the worst has happened, I daresay we'll get something quite grand."

"So the thief wouldn't have had to lower himself melodramatically from the ceiling on a steel cable, like Michael Caine?" asked another *Topkapi* fan.

"Oh dear no," said Miss Lilly. "In fact, on this particular night—last night, that is, though it seems longer ago somehow—it appears that all the thief had to do was open the door, walk in, and help himself." The white chignon quivered with indignation.

"But surely your night watchman—" objected Morrisroe of Art History, "what's his name? Thompson—"

"Our night watchman, Bennie Thompson, is a most reliable young man," said Miss Lilly firmly. "It appears that he was simply in another part of the building when it happened. It's a big place, of course, and he can't be everywhere at once. Also, our alarm system, such as it is, was never activated, goodness knows why, so Bennie had no reason to think anything was wrong in that workroom. When he finally got there, in the normal course of his rounds, he realized that some of the Aegean Gold was missing and called the police at once."

"Miss Lilly," asked Antonia, "what about the daggers, the Shaft Grave daggers? Were they . . . ?"

"Ah, Antonia, there you are!" There was just the slightest suggestion of relief in Miss Lilly's voice. Here at least was someone who would take a properly serious view of the situation.

"It's an odd business, really," Miss Lilly continued. "I was telling Mr. Greenfield about it just a few minutes ago. This thief, for the most part, took pretty much what one would expect—several gold cups and goblets, a silver jug, quite a lot of gold jewelry, a diadem—in short, what was most portable and most obviously valuable. But there are two rather curious exceptions. One is a large ceramic jar from Knossos, decorated with typical Minoan reliefs of bulls' heads and double axes. It isn't a particularly attractive piece, though of course it's of great historical interest. But to the layman's eye it must be rather unappealing, covered with cracks and patches and crude faded pictures. Even more to the point, it's quite heavy and bulky—it stands nearly three feet tall. If, as we assume, the thief packed the smaller gold and silver objects inside it to leave his hands free, it must have weighed close to fifty pounds when he walked out of the museum with it."

"He was taking quite a risk, too, wasn't he?" asked the English T.A. "I mean, he could hardly conceal it under his coat, could he? He must have been conspicuous as a dinosaur, walking around with a thing like that."

"But the daggers, Miss Lilly," Antonia urged gently.

"I'm just coming to them, dear. They are the second exception I mentioned. But in this case, the odd thing is that the thief *didn't* take them!"

Antonia breathed a sigh of relief.

"What he did take," Miss Lilly went on, "was a *reproduction* of the most famous of all the daggers, the Lion Hunt Blade from Mycenae. The originals, of course, have mostly lost their gold hilts, and the bronze blades are badly corroded after three and a half millennia. But the lovely inlays are in perfect condition, and they are among the most popular of Bronze Age artifacts. Students, collectors, the general public, archaeologists, and art historians—everyone finds them irresistible."

"Yet this thief of yours," Morrisroe cut in, "somehow contrived to resist them, and took a more or less worthless modern copy instead. Plain gross ignorance is the answer to that little puzzle, I should think."

"Perhaps, Mr. Morrisroe," said Miss Lilly, "though I would hardly call the copy worthless. It's meticulously accurate, of course, and beautifully executed, and I daresay it could be sold to some unscrupulous collector for several hundred dollars. But you're right that any one of the originals would bring many times that from the same collector. But what is puzzling is this: why would a thief, so amazingly ignorant as not to realize that a collection of ancient blades, corroded and hiltless though they are, is a hundred times more valuable than a flashy modern reproduction— why would such an uninformed thief go to all the trouble and risk of carrying off a great heavy jar that only the most discriminating collector would be interested in?"

"I see what Miss Lilly means," said Antonia thoughtfully. "A thief smart enough, and determined enough, to steal the Knossos jar should have been smart enough to pocket a handful of knives that were just as valuable and a lot easier to fence . . ."

"And a thief dumb enough to pass over the daggers should have been too dumb to bother with the jar!" the dark teaching assistant who had witnessed the uncrating finished triumphantly.

"Precisely," said Miss Lilly.

"But surely this is all a bit academic," put in Win Randolph. "With all the publicity this exhibition has been getting, there must be thousands, tens of thousands of people who would recognize the stolen objects. We've been bombarded with pictures of them in newspapers, magazines, television for weeks now. Surely these things won't get very far before someone spots them."

"Yes, that's what the police are saying too," said Miss Lilly without much enthusiasm. "They're quite optimistic, in fact. Or so they say."

"You yourself are *not* optimistic, then?"

Words, for the first time in anyone's memory, failed Miss Lilly. But the faculty rallied around and plied her with reassurances, expressions of confidence in detectives and insurance investigators, and encouraging anecdotes about previous art thefts. By the time Antonia slipped quietly away, Miss Lilly was looking considerably less ravaged by the morning's ordeal.

Antonia herself, as she walked back through the deserted corridors to her office, tried to sort out a confused set of reactions. Concern for the lost Aegean Gold and sympathy for Miss Lilly and the other museum officials struggled with a skeptical sense of the improbability of the situation. Odds and ends of irreplaceable ancient gold just lying about loose in a workshop somewhere in the bowels of a great museum? A security guard who didn't happen to notice that someone was stealing them? There was a certain musical-comedy implausibility to the whole thing when you stopped to think about it.

Then she remembered her twelve-thirty appointment with Ariadne and abruptly ceased to think of the museum burglary as a Sigmund Romberg absurdity. Her last thought before she opened her office door was: *I must break this gently to Ariadne. She won't have heard, and she'll be terribly upset.*

Antonia waited until almost one o'clock, but the girl never appeared. Antonia thereupon packed up her briefcase and departed, silently cursing the irresponsibility of graduate students and wondering whether a summer in Crete with a representative of the scatterbrained younger generation was really what she yearned for after all.

A few minutes later she left campus with her colleague Barry Greenfield of the English department. The halcyon weather had inspired him to ask her to share a picnic lunch and a bike tour through Mill Creek Park. An afternoon or evening with Barry was always pleasant, and on such a beautiful day irresistible. She had decided her shopping and sunbathing could wait and accepted gladly.

It was therefore by a margin of about four minutes that she missed the arrival of Detective Lieutenant Steve Caracci, who was annoyed to find that most of the faculty had already left and were not expected back on campus before Monday morning.

He was investigating the museum burglary, of course, and it appeared that he had particularly wanted to question Professor Antonia Nielsen.

❦ 3 ❦

Missing Gold, Missing Girl

FOUR HOURS OF BIKING THROUGH CLOUDS OF DOG-
wood and forsythia, drinking red wine, and eating Barry's
chicken sandwiches put Ariadne's small dereliction into
perspective. By the time Barry deposited her at her apartment around five, she felt pleasantly tired, but distinctly
more mellow.

She was due at the Randolphs for dinner at eight and
was looking forward to it. There would be talk of the un-
seasonable weather, no doubt, but there would also be the
burglary to analyze and speculate about, and surely even
the dullness of an academic dinner party couldn't kill *that*
as a topic of conversation. She just hoped Gillian would be
all right.

She took a long hot shower that left her feeling mar-
velously relaxed and buoyant. Her big Afghan hound, Nike,
laid her muzzle against the crack under the bathroom door
and kept watch until Antonia reappeared. The dog also
found hot showers soothing, provided that she herself was
not required to get wet while admiring the sound of them.

Antonia emerged, her long caramel-colored hair still
piled haphazardly on top of her head, just as the doorbell
rang. Nike gave her single sharp the-doorbell-is-ringing
bark, and together they went to answer it.

It is not recorded which of them was more startled, Antonia at the identification card in the detective's palm, or he at the tall figure in flowing caftan and high-piled hair. Only Nike seemed unabashed at the situation, sniffing politely at the lieutenant's ankle and retreating to the spot before the fireplace where she customarily presided over company gatherings.

"Miss—ah, Professor—Nielsen?"

"Yes?"

"It's about this burglary at the museum, Miss Nielsen. May I . . . ?"

"Of course. Sorry. But I don't quite see . . ."

"Thanks." He closed the door behind him and moved toward an armchair near the fireplace, giving Nike a brief but knowledgeable rub behind the ear before he sat down. The silky plume of Nike's tail moved once in acknowledgment of this tribute, and she gazed adoringly at him throughout the remainder of his stay. Here, clearly, was a man worth cultivating.

"Can I offer you a drink, Lieutenant, or would that be against regulations?"

"No, Ma'am, thanks anyway. Though strictly speaking I am off duty. I missed you this afternoon at the university, and I was passing not too far from here on my way home, so I thought I'd give you another try."

"Of course I'll be glad to help any way I can, but I really don't have a great deal to do with the museum. Surely you aren't going to question the entire university faculty? So, why me?"

"It isn't exactly you we're interested in, Miss Nielsen. It's a student of yours, Ariadne Pappas."

"Ariadne? But why on earth . . . ? She's not really a student of mine. I had her in a seminar once a couple of years ago, that's all."

"Several of your colleagues mentioned that Miss

Pappas is in the habit of coming to your office rather frequently." A faint smile stirred briefly behind Caracci's professional impassivity as he added, " 'Mother confessor' was the expression one of them used to describe you."

"That," said Antonia, "is an exaggeration. Or rather, it's inaccurate. It's true that she's taken to stopping by my office this year—she had an appointment with me this afternoon, in fact. But our conversations are hardly what I'd call confessional. In glaring contrast to most of her contemporaries, Ariadne rarely talks about herself."

"What does she talk about then?"

"Her work. Or rather the subject of her work."

"I'm afraid I don't quite see the difference."

"Well, Lieutenant, what most academics talk about is their work—what *I'm* researching, what *I've* published, what *I'm* trying to accomplish. When she talks at all, Ariadne talks about antiquity. What the Greeks or Romans or Minoans thought and wrote and achieved. I think the Mediterranean world of two or three thousand years ago is a good deal more alive, more real to her than this campus or her fellow students or the academic profession. It borders on the neurotic, in fact, this reverence of hers for things classical. But I still don't see why you're interested in Ariadne."

"As you may know, Professor Nielsen, Miss Pappas has been working part-time at the museum. I understand that several graduate students were hired a few months ago, to free some of the regular staff for work on this exhibition of, ah, Aegean Gold." He pronounced it *Eegian*, knowing he had probably got it wrong.

Antonia did not smile at his gaffe. "I'm sorry," she said, "but I still don't see . . ."

"The stolen objects had been left overnight in a kind of workroom or large office where the student employees have their desks. There seems to be some evidence that

Miss Pappas was working late last night in that room. She didn't come to work this afternoon, and no one we've been able to locate so far has seen her since she left the museum at regular closing time yesterday."

"Lieutenant," Antonia burst out indignantly, "if you are implying—"

Ignoring the interruption, Caracci went on imperturbably. "You say the girl had an appointment with you this afternoon. Did she keep it?"

"No," said Antonia reluctantly.

"And what was the purpose of this appointment? Since she's not in any of your classes at present . . ."

"That's right. I don't know why she bothered to make an appointment, actually. It was unusual. Normally she just drops in when she happens to be in the building. I don't think she has many friends, and she's probably lonely. But yesterday she stopped by on the way to her job and asked if she could see me today at twelve-thirty."

"But she never showed up."

"No. But really, Lieutenant—"

"I know, Miss Nielsen, I know." Caracci's voice sounded a little weary. "This student couldn't possibly be involved in the burglary, she isn't the type, etc." He held up a restraining hand as Antonia opened her mouth to protest once more.

"Miss Nielsen, we're not accusing your student of anything. As a matter of fact I don't see her as a very promising suspect myself. From what the museum people have told us, she's conscientious, reliable, responsible—everything you could ask for in an employee. But the fact remains that she was with those objects last night, the night of the burglary, she failed to show up for work and for an appointment today, and she can't be located now. There's probably some explanation, but you can't expect us to ignore all that simply because her friends assure us she's not the type to steal things."

"No, of course not, Lieutenant. Sorry if I sounded defensive." Antonia was feeling slightly foolish. Why on earth had she leaped to the defense of Ariadne, who presumably needed no defending?

"Don't apologize, Miss Nielsen. Most people, especially the innocent ones, get a little uptight at the idea of themselves or their friends being questioned by the police. But we do need to talk to Miss Pappas."

At this point Nike rose with great dignity from her spot before the fireplace, padded over to Caracci's chair, and laid her muzzle suggestively across his knee. He rubbed absently behind her ear as Antonia too stood up.

"Sure you won't change your mind about that drink, Lieutenant? I'm going to make myself one."

"No, thanks," said Caracci, "I'll be leaving in just a minute. But you go right ahead." By the time Antonia returned, highball in hand, the expression on the Afghan's face was one of blissful and oblivious idiocy. Antonia smiled at the two of them.

"Well, Lieutenant," she said, "you seem to have made quite an impression on old Nike. She's a pushover for anyone who knows how to rub ears properly."

"Yes, Ma'am. Dogs do seem to like me as a rule. Well—" He straightened up in his chair with a back-to-business air and Nike collapsed on his shoes with a contented sigh. "About the Pappas girl. Do you have any idea where she might be?"

"I'm afraid I can't help you much there." Antonia glanced at her watch. "At six o'clock on a Friday evening, I suppose she would normally be in her apartment. But presumably you've covered that."

"Yes, Ma'am. Of course we'll try again later."

"Well, she could be working in the library. She's up against a dissertation deadline in about four weeks. And I think she has a family living somewhere in the city."

"A mother and a sister. We've talked to them too. They weren't exactly cordial, but they claim they haven't seen her for several weeks. They're supposed to let us know if she shows up there."

"As I said, I have the impression that Ariadne doesn't have many friends, but she must have a few, and I suppose she could be with one of them. I can't give you any specific names, unfortunately. Wait—I think she had a roommate last year. The girl moved out some time ago, but I believe they may still see each other occasionally. The dean of graduate students could track down her name for you, I expect."

"Well, every little bit helps," said Caracci with as little enthusiasm as originality.

"You've talked to Professor Randolph? He's directing Ariadne's dissertation—probably meets with her once a month or so. I suppose he knows her as well as anyone on the faculty, though as you can see that isn't saying a whole lot."

"Yes, I talked to him just before coming here. He wasn't able to tell me much either. He gives pretty much the same picture of this girl as you do—hardworking, lonely, uncommunicative, a bit screwy on the subject of antiquity."

Antonia winced at the last of his adjectives. It could be a direct quote from Win Randolph for all she knew, Win being somewhat given to sarcastic hyperbole where students were concerned.

" 'Screwy' is putting it rather strongly, Lieutenant," she said, trying not to sound offended. "Ariadne doesn't distort realities, ancient or modern. In fact, in some ways she's a very hardheaded practical person. I suspect she's had to be, to survive at all. It's only on this one point that she—I guess you could say she overidentifies. I know, I know," she added in response to the disapproving expression that was coming over Caracci's face, "that sounds like psychiatric jargon. But it's the right word for Ariadne's relationship with the ancient world. She functions very well as a twentieth-century American student. But her deepest loyalties, and all the bottled-up enthusiasm one senses in her—they go to her remote ancestors. She speaks of the streets and gates and markets of Athens and Knossos as you or I might speak of Wall Street or Central Park. They have an uncanny kind of *reality* for her that I can't really describe. You'll see what I mean when you meet her."

"Yes. Well, that's exactly what I'm trying to do, Miss Nielsen, meet her."

"You may find Ariadne a disappointment when she *does* turn up. You can't be as certain as I am that she had nothing to do with the burglary, I suppose. But as for her noticing anything fishy going on around the museum— well, I'm doubtful. She isn't very alert to people and things around her. More than once she's passed me on campus without speaking or seeming to notice I was there. It's not intentional, I'm quite sure—when she sees me, she's always very cordial. But there are times when her mind is just— elsewhere."

"But from your description of her, I should think any threat, any suspicion of a threat, to the museum's treasures would be the one thing she *would* be alert to."

Antonia was startled at his perception. He hadn't seemed to be listening so closely to what she had told him of Ariadne. Apparently he understood the girl better than she had given him credit for.

"Point for you, Lieutenant," she conceded. "If there was anything of that sort to be noticed, Ariadne probably would have noticed it. But isn't it hoping for rather a lot— a squint-eyed stranger skulking about the museum, I mean?"

"Yes, Ma'am." For the first time Caracci grinned. "We don't get too many of those types nowadays. It'd make our job too easy, I expect." He moved toward the door, escorted by the still-hopeful Nike. "But sometimes a small thing, something less melodramatic than your squint-eyed stranger —you'd be surprised what people can remember sometimes if you prod their memory a bit."

"I suppose so. Although it doesn't seem to have worked that way in my case," she added ruefully.

"Don't worry about it, Miss Nielsen. We'll talk to her when she turns up." He gave Nike's silky head a farewell pat at the door.

After he had gone, Antonia gulped the last of her watery Scotch and for a few moments stared unseeing out the window at the darkening street below. Nike came silently up behind her, leaned companionably against her right thigh, and looked out too.

"I don't like it, old girl," Antonia mused, "I don't like it. Ariadne Pappas, of all people, vanishing like a magician's rabbit just when—oh, it's preposterous."

And she disappeared into the bedroom to dress for Gillian Randolph's party. Nike remained at the window, gazing at the shifting patterns of lights from the traffic below.

4

"They Never Get Any Older!"

THE SALAD GREENS WERE VERY CRISP, THE CRUST OF the quiche Lorraine very flaky, the white wine superbly dry. Gillian herself, as usual on such occasions, was in her element. Though she was not a beautiful woman, few men were aware of the fact. She was wearing one of the fluid jersey dresses that she collected so assiduously and that softened her rather angular figure. This particular specimen was black, which had the additional advantage of setting off the masses of dark red hair draped elegantly about her head. The sleek mahogany coils in turn distracted one's attention from her long equine face.

Antonia, on more than one previous occasion, had found herself neglecting her own food as she gazed hypnotically at Gillian's hands. Once again they were transforming the most mundane of tasks into a kind of ballet, the long slender fingers gliding deftly among silver and porcelain, lifting a slice of quiche, transferring salad from bowl to plate.

Her voice rose gaily above the flatter American intonations of her guests, its accent carefully preserved from her days as a scholarship student at Cambridge's Girton College. Win, on the other hand, took little part in the conversation. Antonia had long suspected that he deliberately effaced himself in favor of his wife at such affairs, preferring to let her exercise her social gifts as fully as possible. She had few enough opportunities to do so, as Win had once ruefully remarked to Antonia. The least he could do was let her make the most of them.

She was making the most of them now. Antonia had rarely seen her so vivacious. The combination of the wine, the company, and the excitement of the museum burglary seemed to have left her even more exhilarated than usual. She turned now to Roy Sandler, the Classics chairman, and inquired:

"I suppose the Aegean Gold exhibition will have to be postponed now, won't it? What a pity!"

"No, as a matter of fact our unsinkable Miss Lilly assures me that 'The Show Will Go On.' I even suspect, though I didn't say so to her, that the burglary may actually give the exhibition a certain *succès de scandale*."

"Hardly the sort of publicity to appeal to poor Miss Lilly," observed Renée Gatineau sympathetically.

"No, of course not," said Sandler. "Still, if it brings in a few extra dollars . . ."

"Perhaps they could be applied toward her new security system for the museum," suggested Pierre Gatineau. "There would be in that a certain poetic justice."

"There would indeed," said Sandler, "but I'm afraid poetic justice isn't exactly what the financial administration of this institution is famous for."

"Well," said his wife, Martha, "at least the Faculty Women's Club won't have to reschedule its Spring Outing. We've persuaded Professor Morrisroe to give us a lecture tour of the exhibition, you know. And after what I've been through trying to get the whole thing organized . . ."

Martha Sandler, a plump and motherly woman in her early fifties, was as renowned for her nonstop tongue as for her kindly and sympathetic heart. Her husband, after thirty

years of practice, had become adept at spotting her mono-
logues in their early stages. He seemed to sense one approaching now, and with the kindest of intentions moved
to forestall it.

Turning to his host, he asked, "It's odd about the
Pappas girl, isn't it, Win? What do you make of the cops'
interest in her?"

Win, who had been gazing at the centerpiece, looked
startled. "I didn't make anything of it," he said irritably.
"Just assumed they were covering the whole museum staff,
I suppose."

"I'm not so sure," said Sandler. "When they talked to
me, they seemed pretty interested in her financial situation."

"Nonsense!" snorted Win. "Ariadne Pappas swiping
ancient artifacts to pay her grocery bills—now *there* is a
deduction worthy of our local gendarmerie! If you ask me,"
he added abruptly, "the whole thing is nothing but an
outbreak of *febris vernalis* among our clean-limbed young
seekers after wisdom. In short, a student prank."

"Oh, come on, Win, surely you don't . . ."

"I mean it. I fully expect to wake up one morning and
find Clytemnestra's diadem gracing the brazen brow of
President Higgenbotham's statue in the Quad."

"What is *febris varn*—what he said?" inquired Martha
Sandler.

"It means spring fever," Antonia replied. "Or so he
imagines. But I'm afraid there's more to it than that, Win.
The police really *are* interested in Ariadne—they grilled me
about her too."

Gillian had temporarily withdrawn from the conversation to dispense second helpings and refill wine glasses, not
forgetting her own. When she spoke now there was an odd
metallic edge to her voice that Win and Antonia recognized
instantly.

"Quite a lot of people seem to find this Ariadne Pappas a very—*interesting* girl. Up from the slums and all that. Smoldering Mediterranean eyes too, I shouldn't wonder."

Win muttered, "Now, Gillian, don't start . . ."

Roy Sandler managed a fair show of casual heartiness as he said, "Really, Gillian, have you ever actually met the girl? She's hardly the femme fatale type."

"Possibly not," said Gillian, "but I have yet to meet an American student who wasn't irresponsible, self-centered, and . . ."

"That's true," put in Antonia, "of a good many of them. But Ariadne's a different breed entirely. She's conscientious and responsible to a fault."

But Gillian was not to be placated. "Well, *I* don't call it responsible behavior when a girl rings up at . . ."

Win interrupted her with greater urgency this time: "Gillian, *please* . . ."

Taking his turn in the attempt to pour oil on the ruffled waters, Pierre Gatineau said, "While I cannot agree with Win that the burglary itself was a student prank, still there may be something in the idea of spring fever. The campus was delicious this afternoon, with the—" he turned to his wife, Renée "—*cornouiller?*"

"Dogwood, *chéri.*"

"Yes, dogwood. And the daffodils and the student girls in their swim costumes. This girl, this Ariadne—perhaps she also has succumbed to the *ambience* and simply departed for the weekend?"

But his efforts too were doomed to failure. At the mention of sunbathing coeds, Gillian's face took on an expression of triumphant disapproval. The moral depravity of Ariadne Pappas and her kind had obviously been demonstrated to *her* satisfaction. She said nothing, however, but collected a few dinner plates and disappeared into the kitchen with them.

While she was gone, her guests tried halfheartedly to sustain some semblance of general conversation, but their embarrassment was painfully obvious. After a few minutes, under cover of clearing away the remaining dishes, Antonia followed Gillian into the kitchen.

She was standing at the sink, making a rather unconvincing show of scraping and rinsing the dinner plates. A half-empty highball glass stood nearby on the Formica countertop. Gillian glanced up as the kitchen door swung closed behind Antonia, then turned back to her drink. She spoke over the rim of her glass while Antonia set her offering of plates and salad bowls on the counter.

"I daresay you all think I'm making a spectacle of myself, don't you? P'raps you're right, too. But what you don't know is what it's like . . ." She paused for another gulp of the rapidly diminishing highball, ". . . what it's like, sitting in this bloody house with practically nothing to do, knowing that your husband is being exposed day after day, year after year, to hundreds of attractive girls who never get any older." She seemed pleased with the phrase, because she repeated it with heavy dramatic emphasis. *"They never get any older."*

At least, thought Antonia, she left out the bits about being exiled three thousand miles from home, and childless. When Gillian brought all her big guns to bear simultaneously, she could be quite impossible.

"Really, Gillian," she said, "aren't you being a bit melodramatic? Win, as you well know, is devoted to you. And Roy is quite right about Ariadne Pappas—she's just not a likely candidate for the role of homewrecker."

"No?" Gillian's voice was almost arch. She had reached, Antonia judged, the game-playing stage where the contest was more of wits than emotions. Gillian was right about herself in one respect: she was an idle, aimless woman, bored to distraction, and a lively argument would probably give her a good deal of satisfaction. Even one designed to demonstrate her husband's infidelity.

"No," said Antonia firmly, "and you must stop this. You're beginning to sound like something out of Albee."

"You mean Martha, I suppose. The one with the emotional maturity of a twelve year old."

"Exactly. And it isn't worthy of you." She hurried on before Gillian could reply. "Look, I sympathize with what you said about American students. I get pretty turned off by them myself at times But this Pappas girl really is different. I'm not sure she's interested in men of any kind, let alone married ones nearly twice her age. She's so wrapped up in her work she's hardly aware of anyone, of either sex. And as for Win, if he were going to philander—which I doubt—it wouldn't be with Ariadne."

"Why not? I suppose you're going to tell me she's plain and frumpy."

"No, not frumpy." How to describe Ariadne to one who had never seen her? The "Mediterranean" eyes did indeed "smolder," in Gillian's words—though almost certainly not for Gillian's husband. And the sweep of black hair, though it needed a little shaping and a lot of brushing —no, "mousy" was definitely not the word for it either.

Finally, Antonia said, "It's just that she makes it so obvious, so blatantly obvious, that she's not interested— not in sex, not in anything outside her work—that most men would be instantly repelled, I think."

"But even a girl like that—so keen on her work and all—they've been thrown together so much. Win's her dissertation director, he's *part* of her work."

"You mustn't think in terms of a British tutorial, Gillian. The relationship between student and dissertation director here is often pretty tenuous. Some directors, with a student as independent as Ariadne, might not meet her more than two or three times all year. With Win and

Ariadne, I don't know, I suppose they get together about once a month. And that's hardly enough to wear down resistance as massive as hers."

There were other and more compelling reasons why the girl could not possibly be interested in Win Randolph, though they could hardly be conveyed to Gillian. One had only to look at them to see the impossibility—at Win's loose-limbed casual elegance, every inch of him the conventional tweed-and-suede professor, and at Ariadne with her tense lean figure like a coiled whip. . . .

"Well," Gillian interrupted her thoughts, "they've obviously been seeing a good deal more of each other than *that!*" The note of triumphant self-vindication had returned to her voice, and she pulled a piece of paper from her apron pocket and waved it under Antonia's nose.

"I found this in the pocket of his winter coat yesterday morning. And you needn't fancy I was prying, either. With the weather so warm, he'd worn just a light jacket to the office, and I thought I could get the coat cleaned before it turned cold again. I was just emptying the pockets to take it to the cleaner." She thrust the paper at Antonia.

"Really, Gillian, I don't want . . ."

"Go on, read it. You'll see what I mean." The distant note of hysteria was creeping into her voice again, and Antonia was reluctant to aggravate her. She took the note.

> *Dear Win,*
>
> *If you keep pressuring me like this, I will have no choice but to tell someone what is going on. You seem to think I couldn't go on without you, but if I have to I will.*
>
> *Can't you see how much this means to me—much more than it possibly can to you? I am doing this for love, however it may look to other people.*
>
> *Please stop by Thursday night so that we can settle things once and for all.*
>
> *Ariadne*

"What I see," said Antonia, handing back the note, "is that she calls him Win, as most of the doctoral students do—graduate students of both sexes. He encourages it, Gillian, and it's not uncommon these days anyway. But more importantly, I see an overwrought girl in the final throes of writing her dissertation, who has probably had a chapter criticized or even rejected outright and has over-reacted. It's a well-known syndrome. Knowing both Ariadne and Win, I emphatically do not see in it what you apparently do. The men Ariadne Pappas gets passionately involved with, Gillian, have been dead for three thousand years."

"But that peremptory tone, the familiarity of it—it's insufferable. This is the outburst of an exasperated lover, Antonia, not a student."

It was the outburst, Antonia thought, of a tired, neurotic student who had probably not had much respect for her professor to begin with, and by now was in an advanced state of exhaustion, anxiety, and frustration.

Aloud she said, "I know the state she's in, Gillian, from the inside as well as the outside. When I was finishing my dissertation I lost fifteen pounds, shouted at my director, had nightmares about him—in short, acted thoroughly unbalanced. And I've seen Ariadne, and she's been looking haggard and anxious for the last few weeks. It's a very difficult time for a student, Gillian. Try to understand."

Before Gillian could reply, Win came through the swinging door into the kitchen. "Gillian's feeling a little upset right now, Win," said Antonia. "I think she should lie down for a while. You and I could serve the dessert and coffee, couldn't we?"

"Yes, of course, but . . ." He turned anxiously to his wife. "What is it, Gillian? Surely you're not upset about this wretched Pappas girl?"

"*My* feelings are hardly the issue," retorted Gillian,

brandishing Ariadne's note. "The question is, how serious are *you* two?"

Even though half the note was concealed by Gillian's long fingers, Win seemed to recognize it and relax. "So that's where it was—I'd been wondering where it had gotten to. But I don't see why that note should upset you, Gillian."

"That's funny, Antonia has the same problem. She can't see what it has to do with me either. You both seem to think I'm blind, deaf, and dumb. V*ery* dumb, apparently."

"Darling, let's discuss it later. Antonia's right, you ought to rest for a bit." He put his arm around Gillian's shoulders and started toward the kitchen's second door, which opened into a back stairway to the upper floor of the house, but Gillian twisted away from him.

"I don't want to rest," she whispered, her long equine face suddenly contorted with fury. "What I want is for you to keep your *hands* off those bloody little . . . bloody little . . ."

Gillian had kept her voice low to avoid being overheard by her guests in the next room. But Antonia recognized the tone. She and Win and a handful of others had heard it just once before.

About nine months before, in fact, at a Fourth of July picnic given by the Sandlers. Gillian had come upon Win talking and laughing with an attractive blond graduate student in an out-of-the-way corner of the garden. Antonia, to her chagrin, had been standing nearby and could not avoid witnessing the whole incident. It must, she assumed, have been the culmination of a long period of tension, frustration, and suppressed anger between Win and Gillian, but that climactic moment was all she or anyone else saw, and to the startled onlookers it appeared as sudden and savage as a flash flood.

So shocking had the scene been, both in its ugliness and in its incongruity with the decorous little academic picnic, that Antonia could remember only isolated fragments of it with any clarity.

Gillian, in the same low-pitched but vicious tone she was using now, calling the bewildered student a bloody little bitch.

Gillian's long pale fingers around the girl's throat.

Gillian's expression, a mixture of relief and baffled fury as Win pulled her off and led her unresisting to their car.

It had been several weeks before Gillian had appeared in public again. Antonia was one of the few who knew that this temporary withdrawal was due to more than just mortification at the spectacle she had made of herself.

A few hours after Win had taken her home, Gillian had tried to kill herself.

Both Win and Antonia were painfully aware of the whole episode as they stood now in Gillian's kitchen, embarrassed and baffled. But their dilemma was resolved, suddenly and unexpectedly, by Gillian herself. Though she still stood as if at bay, her back against the refrigerator, the look of animal rage passed from her face as abruptly as it had appeared. When she spoke to her husband again, her voice was stiff and formal but calm.

"I'm sorry, Win. I expect you think I've overreacted. All right, we'll just drop it for the time being. One has to solve one's own problems in one's own way, of course, and I'm afraid I tend to forget that at times. Sorry." She glanced around her kitchen as if reminding herself where she was and what needed to be done next. Plunging into the refrigerator, she extracted from it a chocolate mousse evidently intended as the evening's *pièce de résistance*. Then, with a coolness that was almost arrogant, she said,

"Just bring the coffee in for me, would you, Antonia?" And she swept out of the kitchen without a backward glance.

"Think she'll be all right?" said Antonia after a moment.

"I don't know," said Win unhappily as he unplugged the electric coffee pot. "What on earth was in that note to set her off? Something about meeting me to hash out the last chapter of the dissertation? It came—let's see—almost a week ago, and needless to say I didn't memorize the damn thing."

"The tone is a bit intense, that's all. I tried to explain about predoctoral melancholia, but I don't think she bought it."

"She wouldn't, no. People—which by courtesy includes students—are supposed to have stiffer upper lips than that, in Gillian's view." He started for the door, coffee pot in hand. "We'll just have to muddle through the rest of the evening and hope for the best."

With some misgivings Antonia followed him into the dining room.

Shortly before midnight she returned to her apartment, where Nike greeted her sleepily with two slow waves of her tail before dozing off again.

The tensions of the Randolphs' dinner party, coming on top of the physical fatigue of a long afternoon of biking, had left Antonia feeling utterly drained. For a moment she considered the tempting possibility of simply collapsing on the floor beside Nike and losing consciousness until morning. But that, she told herself firmly, would probably mean a backache tomorrow, and besides the dog had to be walked. It was even possible that a stroll on the quiet campus would have a soothing effect.

They set out toward the university campus, Nike trotting briskly ahead with an occasional glance over her shoulder to make sure Antonia hadn't strayed. Nike loved the campus because it was the only place within walking distance of their apartment where she could really stretch her legs, and their walk was the high point of her day.

They took their standard thirty-minute tour, which comprised the library, the physics building, the administration building, and the student center, and ended at the museum. They had almost reached it, and Antonia was about to turn back toward home, when Nike suddenly froze at attention, a warning rumble rising in her throat, legs stiff and muzzle pointing tensely toward the museum.

Assuming that the source of the dog's excitement was a bird or squirrel, Antonia started to pull her back along the path. But then she too noticed something moving in the shadows at the base of the dark mass that was the museum. It was hardly more than a shadow itself, but it was certainly not a small animal. For an instant Antonia wondered if a bear had escaped from the zoo and was prowling the campus. But then the thing rose to its full height—it must have been bending over, looking at something on the ground—and she could see that it was a man. A huge, shapeless figure, but definitely a man, perhaps one of the varsity football players. He moved clumsily but swiftly away, around the museum, till the corner of the building hid him from view.

Nike, who took her responsibilities seriously, continued to grumble discontentedly deep in her throat for a while, but eventually decided the peril had passed and it was safe to return to her detailed examination of the nearby shrubbery. She took Antonia home a few minutes later, without further incident.

5

Night People

ANTONIA SPENT SATURDAY MORNING SHOPPING FOR her Aegean Gold dress. She found it at last, a shimmering cascade of narrow white pleats from neckline to hem. When she stood very still it made her feel like a Doric temple column, and when she moved she thought she looked like an Alpine waterfall. Naturally, a dress that could do all that was not to be resisted, and she bought it.

She devoted two hours in the middle of the day to the beginnings of the tan that the temple-column-waterfall dress clearly called for. By two o'clock she was in her office, putting finishing touches to the overdue article. She spent three blissful hours retouching her prose, verifying a few footnotes, and composing a cover letter to the *Classical Journal* editor. When at last she could find nothing more that seemed to require polishing, she gave the article a quick read-through to judge its overall effect, and was pleased. With a great sense of satisfaction she laid it on the department secretary's desk to be mailed Monday morning. The feeling accompanied her all the way home across the fragrant campus.

When she reached her apartment at five o'clock, there was a young black man sprawled on the floor outside her door.

HE SAT THERE, back to the wall, long legs jackknifed because the corridor was too narrow to allow him to extend them full length, the toes of his battered boots braced against the opposite wall. His head hung limply at a grotesque angle, in the manner of those who fall asleep sitting bolt upright. As Antonia bent down to reassure herself that he really was only sleeping, her long hair must have brushed his cheek, because he leaped up with a startled cry.

He stood before her, one hand on his neck, turning his head stiffly from side to side, looking disoriented but unembarrassed. He was very tall and lean, and had an air of having been carelessly assembled: the various parts of his body, though decently shaped and well proportioned in themselves, gave the impression of having only tenuous connections with one another, as if he might fall apart at any moment.

"Miss Nielsen? My name's Bennie Thompson. I'm a friend of Ariadne Pappas."

Antonia had the door unlocked by now, but she turned at the mention of Ariadne's name. "Have you seen her? Do you know where she is?"

Before Bennie could answer, something dark and shapeless and very large exploded from the apartment door, striking Bennie squarely in the chest and hurling him violently back against the wall of the corridor. He slid slowly down the wall into a sitting position reminiscent of the one he had just quitted.

"Down, Nike! That's enough, get down!" Antonia's voice was stern, but there was a hint of amusement in it. The big Afghan, after giving Bennie's nose one solicitous lick, padded docilely back into the apartment and sat down with a sigh just inside the door.

"Sorry, Mr. Thompson. She probably thought she was

protecting my life and limbs. At any rate, she wouldn't have hurt you. If she decided you were dangerous, she'd just sit on your chest pending further instructions. If she chose to regard you as a friend, she'd do the same thing out of pure affection. She must have known you were out here—they're hounds, you know, keen noses and all that. How long *have* you been here, by the way?"

Bennie had struggled to his feet for the second time in three minutes and was massaging one shoulder, which had hit the wall with considerable force. The expression of astonishment and fear that had swept over his face when the dog lunged at him was giving way to one of annoyance. "I dunno. Couple of hours, I guess. I remember now, she barked once when I rang the bell but I fell asleep after that. Forgot there was a dog in there."

Antonia, feeling more secure now that Nike was around, gestured to Bennie Thompson to enter the apartment. He walked in with a nervous glance at the dog and stood uneasily in the middle of Antonia's small living room. She followed him in, closing the door behind her.

"Well, Mr. Thompson," she repeated, "*have* you seen Ariadne?"

"No, Ma'am," he said wearily, "I haven't, not since Wednesday night. I was sort of hoping maybe *you* had. Looks like I come all this way for nothing." He sounded resentful.

"No, wait a minute, Mr. Thompson. Let's not give up quite so fast. You say you saw her Wednesday night. Where?"

"In the museum. I work there, see, night watchman, eleven to seven. That's how I met Ari." With a significant glance at Antonia's comfortable-looking armchair he added, "And that's why I flaked out on your doorstep like that. Afternoons, see, that's when I usually do my sleeping."

Taking the hint and motioning him into a chair, Antonia said, "But what on earth would she be doing in the museum at that hour of the night?" She could hear Bennie draw a deep breath before he answered.

"She's been working there at night a lot lately. Not her regular job for the museum, that's in the afternoon. Something of her own."

"Something of her own. That would be her dissertation, presumably. But why in heaven's name in the museum, and after midnight? Did she ever talk to you about what she was doing?"

"No, Ma'am. But it ain't hard to figure why she was doing it in the museum. It's this apartment she's got. I saw it once, and it's really godawful. Plaster falling off the walls, and roaches, and a filthy bathroom on a different floor. Got so she couldn't stand to be in the place except to sleep. So she comes to work in the afternoon and then leaves for a while and eats and comes back around eleven. She has a key to the side door of the museum so she can let herself in. Then she does her own thing all night and goes home about five or six in the morning and sleeps until noon. Like I said, that's how I come to know her. She has a coffee pot, and I stop by her office a couple times a night and we rap awhile. Helps keep us awake."

"So naturally after the burglary Thursday night Ariadne became a prime suspect. They must have assumed . . ."

"No, Ma'am," Bennie interrupted. "You got it all wrong. The fuzz got no special suspicions of Ariadne, as far as I can see. I never said nothing to them about her hanging around the museum at night. Leastways," he added darkly, "not yet."

"I'm afraid I'm not following you."

Bennie sighed, whether from fatigue or from exasperation at Antonia's obtuseness she couldn't tell. "Ari don't want anyone to know she's spending nights in the museum, see. I don't know why, she ain't hurting nothing, but she's always after me not to talk about it. So I promised her."

"You said nothing about this to the police? They've questioned you too?"

"Yeah, Thursday night after the break-in. I didn't say nothing then, but I can't wait much longer. I come here to see if maybe you knew where I could find her—tell her she's gotta tell the cops about this whatever-it-is or else I will. But it looks like you don't know any more'n me. So . . ."

"But if they *don't* suspect Ariadne, then why . . . ?"

"Look, Professor, what this all adds up to is the fuzz ain't got a clue who ripped off that stuff outa the museum, and I'm the handiest one to pin it on. And that I *don't* need," he finished bitterly. "So all right, I promised Ari I wouldn't blab about her being in the museum at weird hours—but there's limits, dammit."

"In other words, Mr. Thompson," Antonia put in angrily, "not to put too fine a point on it, if Ariadne doesn't show up pretty soon and explain herself to the cops, you'll do it for her. And that, you figure, will put her right at the top of the suspect list. Which at the moment consists of just one name—yours."

"Now hold on, Professor, don't you go making me out some kinda monster or something. I'm trying to do right by Ari, but the fact is she *has* been acting real peculiar lately, and that stuff *did* disappear outa the very same room she's been working in, and she *ain't* been seen since. And maybe all that don't mean nothing and then again maybe it do, but either way it's gonna look a whole lot like withholding information from the cops if I just happen to forget to mention what she's been up to. I ain't exactly on their Forty Top Favorites list already, Professor, and I got no mind to put my head in no noose, even for Ari."

"All right, all right, take it easy, Mr. Thompson. I see what you mean. But you know Ariadne—surely *you* don't think . . ."

"Couple months ago, I would of said no way. But now —I dunno, Professor, I still say something funny's going down in that museum. But Ari and that gold stuff—naw, she never would of done nothing like that. She's a funny chick and she could sure use some extra bread, but she'd never rip off the museum to get it. The stuff in that museum, it's like holy relics or something to her. One night she took me around and showed me some of the stuff they got stored away that nobody ever sees. Old hunks of stone with carving on 'em, mostly, and busted clay pots—millions of busted pots. That junk sure didn't turn *me* on, but you shoulda seen what it did for *her*. Like somebody turned on a big light bulb somewhere inside her skull and it come shining out through those black eyes of hers. That is one fine-looking chick, y'know that, Professor? I never noticed it before that night. She mostly goes around with her head down and a kinda scared look—or maybe just tired—and wearing some grungy old shirt. She looks like a real bear, mosta the time. But that night, with that light bulb behind her eyes and her whole face sorta lit up—Jeez, she was somethin' else!"

He paused for a moment, remembering.

"Naw, she never would of ripped off no museum," he repeated. "But she might be into something—I dunno— something funny."

"Why do you say that?"

"There was this one time—I ain't told the fuzz yet because I would of had to tell them about Ari hanging around there nights—but about a month ago I was making my first round—a little before midnight, that'd be—and I come down to the basement level. When I opened the door into the corridor where Ari's office is, I heard her talking to someone in her room. Couldn't hardly hear her voice, she talks so low, but there was a man in there with her and I could hear *him* loud and clear."

"Could you tell what they were talking about?"

"Naw, not really. I heard the guy say, 'I never asked you for nothing,' something like that. But they musta heard me coming down the hall, because they stopped talking all of a sudden. When I got to Ari's door, it was wide open and I looked in." Bennie paused for a moment, and there was an odd expression on his face.

"Well, Ari was just sitting there at her desk like she always does, with a pencil in her hand and those old yellow papers she uses spread out in front of her. And this dude that'd been hassling her, he was nowhere near her. I mean, he wasn't threatening her or nothing, he was standing half-way across the room beside the big worktable they have in there. When I stuck my head in at the door, he swung around kinda slow like until he was facing me. He didn't say nothing, just looked at me. Man, he was the baddest-looking cat I *ever* saw. He musta weighed two fifty if he weighed a pound, and wasn't none of it fat. I always thought I was pretty tall, but he had two, three inches on me, plus he was twice as wide in every direction.

"But him being so big wasn't what got to me. I seen plenty of big cats before, a lot of 'em are clumsier or dumber than me so they don't worry me none. It was his head. It was like it was bigger'n it shoulda been, even for such a huge dude. And those little tiny eyes—you know what they reminded me of? The eyes on those statues they got in the museum that Ari told me used to be painted but now they're just blank. They look like they're seeing every-thing—or nothing, you can't tell which. That's how this guy looked, like he was seeing everything I'd ever thought, or maybe he didn't even notice I was there. Man, he was spooky."

"But you're supposed to be responsible for security at the museum. Shouldn't you have thrown this person out or reported him or something? Or at least warned Ariadne not to have visitors in the museum at such hours?"

"Hell, Professor, that's easy to say—now. But it wasn't like she was throwing wild parties down there or something. That was the one and only time she ever had anyone in her office after hours that I know of. You know how she is, so quiet and serious—well, it just didn't seem like a big security risk at the time, that's all. Even if the dude was kinda weird looking."

"Yes, I see what you mean," said Antonia. "But under the circumstances I think you ought to tell the police about him now."

"I dunno," said Bennie sullenly, "Caracci ain't gonna buy it, not from me. He'll most likely think I'm trying to turn the heat offa me and onto Ariadne or the stranger. Might even think I'm making the whole thing up—wouldn't put it past him."

"You know Lieutenant Caracci, then?"

"Yes, Ma'am." The boy's voice was unmistakably bitter now. "Him and me are old—friends. Except he don't exactly trust me."

"Well, you've got to tell him about this unidentified man anyway. If he's simply a friend of Ariadne's, the police will find it out. You and I know, even if they don't, that Ariadne must be innocent. We *don't* know that he is."

"I guess you're right. And if this dude is making some kinda trouble for Ari, or if he's even mixed up in the burglary, then it'd be better for both of us if the cops brought him in, wouldn't it?"

"Exactly. And if you're still worried about the cops' knowing that Ariadne has been working late at night in the museum—and may even have been there Thursday night —look at it this way: it can hardly make her look worse in

Caracci's eyes than disappearing like this, on the very day of the burglary. To anyone who knows Ariadne, it's only an unfortunate coincidence, but to the rest of the world— including the police—it's a pretty suspicious circumstance, you know."

"Yeah." Antonia was startled to see a malicious grin spread over Bennie's dark face. "Yeah, that's the way their minds work, all right. That's exackly what they *would* figure, ain't it?" And he emitted a laugh that seemed to combine approximately equal parts of derision, contempt, and disgust. It stopped as abruptly as it had begun.

"Awright, I'll go call the lieutenant. I got a pretty good idea what he's gonna say, but after he's said it he'll have to check it out anyway." Wearily, he uncoiled his awkward length from the depths of the armchair. "And Caracci can't hardly say nothing to me I ain't heard from him before."

Antonia closed and locked the door after Bennie Thompson and gave a reassuring pat to Nike, who had escorted him out civilly but with a certain wariness in her manner. She thought briefly about dinner but decided she couldn't face the prospect of cooking. Instead she got herself a beer out of the refrigerator, carried it back into the living room, and flopped down wearily to try to sort out the puzzling events of the last two days.

What exactly had made Bennie Thompson come to her? Concern for Ariadne? Perhaps, in part. But he himself was apparently a prime suspect in the business of the burglary, which tended to cast some doubt on the purity of his motives in mentioning Ariadne's poverty, her familiarity with the museum, her possession of a key to the side door. Worst of all, it had never occurred to anyone, as far as Antonia knew, that Ariadne was in the habit of spending most of the night in the museum, indeed had quite possibly been there on the very night of the burglary. It had never occurred to anyone, that is, until Bennie suggested it. Had he perhaps come to Antonia to give the story a sort of trial run—if she didn't dismiss it out of hand, he would risk trying it on the police?

Moreover, Bennie had hinted strongly that he had a criminal record and that the police fully expected him to get into trouble again sooner or later. Miss Lilly trusted him, and her judgment was not to be lightly dismissed—but on the other hand, how much could she be expected to know about young delinquents? She had probably hired him on a charitable but naive impulse, without realizing the risks she was taking.

Still Antonia shrank from drawing the obvious and uncharitable conclusion concerning Bennie Thompson. At least if he was somehow trying to frame Ariadne or the stranger, or even just distracting attention from himself, he wasn't being especially clever about it. All the details that told against him had been ingenuously called to her attention by Bennie himself. His connection with the museum, of course, was public knowledge. But no one had had any reason to suppose that he had ever so much as heard of Ariadne Pappas—until he volunteered the information. If the missing girl was under suspicion already, as it appeared she was, why would another suspect, eager to clear himself, gratuitously step forth and associate himself with her? Of course, at the same time he might also be attempting to incriminate her still further, but was it worth the risk? The police would no doubt be interested to know that Ariadne had been spending her nights in the museum, but would they not also be intrigued by Bennie's failure to report this fact to the museum authorities weeks ago? He had, by his own account, turned a blind eye to Ariadne's peculiar behavior. Why? What was in it for him? An occasional cup of coffee and a chat to help pass the dreary hours from midnight to 7:00 A.M.? No doubt—but merely that and nothing more?

And why would he invent a grotesque and sinister figure, glimpsed in the museum at an outrageous hour a few weeks before the break-in—and then deliberately undercut the story's effect by suggesting that the police probably wouldn't believe it? It hadn't occurred to her to question the reality of Bennie's Frankenstein monster, until Bennie himself planted the seed of doubt in her mind.

As she rose stiffly from the armchair in which Bennie had been sitting an hour earlier, Antonia decided that the only conclusion justified by this tangle of guesses, suppositions, and unanswered questions was no conclusion at all. The boy might be on the level, genuinely concerned for Ariadne as well as for his own skin—or he might be playing some far more sinister game, the object of which she could see no point in trying to guess at.

So file Bennie for the moment—she simply didn't have enough data on him yet to make a rational assessment. But what about Ariadne, whom she knew well? Now that Caracci wasn't around to see her doubt and uncertainty, Antonia had to admit that it really was a bit much— Ariadne and the Aegean Gold missing at the same time, the gold from the very room in the museum where the girl had been secretly working, presumably against all rules and regulations, until dawn.

Yes, a bit much to be pure coincidence. And yet, unlike Caracci, she did know the girl and she had not been exaggerating when she told the detective it was unthinkable that Ariadne could have stolen the missing pieces of Aegean Gold, poverty or no poverty. Though she hadn't said so to Caracci for fear of seeming to protest too much, in her own mind Antonia was quite certain that the girl would literally starve before she would steal classical artifacts. Perhaps, if Ariadne were desperate enough, she might rob a bank, a liquor store, or a blind beggar, but ancient Greek works of art—never.

So what was the connection between the Aegean Gold and Ariadne—Ariadne, the quintessential loner who seemed to have so little connection with any aspect of the life around her? And yet now suddenly there seemed to be all sorts of connections between Ariadne and other, more ordinary people. Caracci was scouring the city to find her, Bennie—hypothetically at least—was sticking his neck out to protect her, Gillian was hysterically jealous of her.

Antonia became aware that her thoughts were going around like mice on an exercise wheel, whirling faster and faster but never breaking out of the same monotonous circle. She seemed unable to stop thinking, yet was incapable of making her thoughts add up to anything definite or useful.

She forced herself to put it all out of her mind for a while and spent the next couple of hours doing humble but necessary chores around the apartment. She fixed her own and Nike's dinner, washed her hair, and wrote a letter. She gave careful consideration to the dust in the corners and decided it wasn't nearly thick enough yet to justify getting out the vacuum cleaner. Shortly before eight she unplugged the phone, sank blissfully into her deepest armchair with a copy of *Northanger Abbey*, and retired from the world until eleven. When at last she closed the book and drifted slowly back to awareness of her surroundings, Nike rose from her spot by the fireplace, padded over to lay her muzzle on the arm of Antonia's chair, and gazed soulfully into her mistress's eyes.

Antonia got the message.

As usual, the University Museum was the terminus of their nightly walk. Nike knew perfectly well it was the signal to go home, but on this occasion the dog made an elaborate pretense of not recognizing the building or its significance. With a glance at Antonia that dared her to object, the big Afghan turned and galloped madly fifty yards in the wrong direction, then fell into a painstaking examination of the foundation planting around the Math Building.

It was a familiar delaying tactic, but Antonia was in no hurry to get home anyway. Though the night air was cool, it was still prematurely springlike with the rich smells of earth and blossom. There was no moon, but the sky was so clear that crowding stars cast a faint glimmer over shrubbery, footpaths, and college buildings. In the serenity of the silent campus, Antonia found that her thoughts were much clearer and less harried than they had been after Bennie Thompson's departure. Instead of chasing each other around in her head to no purpose, they now marshaled themselves under a few simple headings, and stayed put.

Her instinct was to trust Bennie. Even if some self-serving motives were involved, she had the feeling that his concern for Ariadne was genuine. His story of the girl's late nights in the museum had the ring of truth, too: slaving till dawn over her dissertation in a drafty and deserted building—yes, improbable though it might sound to anyone who didn't know her, that was precisely the sort of thing Ariadne would do.

As for the unlovely visitor Bennie claimed she had entertained there one night—suddenly it occurred to Antonia to identify him with the shadowy figure she herself had glimpsed yesterday evening near the museum. She had dismissed him at the time as one of the more massive forms of student fauna: wrestler, varsity linebacker, something like that. But if there was any chance he was the man

Bennie had found arguing with Ariadne in the museum workroom—well, she would tell Caracci what she had seen and perhaps he would be able to make something of it.

Caracci. Antonia grinned to herself in the dark, a little ruefully. In her present, more mellow mood she suspected she'd done the man less than justice. He'd caught her off guard, turning up unannounced like that, and she'd been unnecessarily prickly in countering what had seemed like attacks on Ariadne. They weren't attacks, of course, but legitimate and probably quite routine questions. In fact, in retrospect she had to admit that Caracci had been scrupulously fair to Ariadne. Next time, Antonia vowed, she would try to be as fair to him. She even found, somewhat to her own surprise, that she was looking forward to that next time.

Rousing herself from her reverie, Antonia looked around for Nike and was about to whistle her in when a shadowy figure came into view near the museum. Two such apparitions on two successive nights, Antonia felt, was really too much, especially in light of Caracci's assurance that skulking strangers were out of style. The next instant, however, she realized her mistake. This was not the same man but someone shorter and much more lightly built.

Another second and she saw that it was Win Randolph. So much for mysterious skulkers.

But as she was about to call out a greeting to Win, something huge and featureless erupted from the shrubbery behind him and seemed to engulf him. Antonia thought she heard a strangled cry of surprise and fear, but there was no other sound. Her heart pounding, she started toward the two figures struggling together on the ground, calling to Nike as she ran.

The Afghan brushed past her at full speed, a gray blur only a few shades lighter than the starlit dimness. As on the previous night, there was a warning rumble in Nike's throat, though Antonia suspected it was more a gesture of good sportsmanship than a serious challenge to the enemy.

Whatever Nike's intentions, her arrival alone was enough to send the attacker on his way. Few men, even large ones, are inclined to argue with sixty pounds of growling dog. This man, at any rate, was not so inclined. With a muttered curse, he made off around the corner of the museum as on the previous night. Nike was clearly longing to chase him, but Antonia called her back and put her on the leash.

"You all right, Win?" Antonia asked a little breathlessly.

"I think so." Understandably enough, he sounded confused as well as scared. "What the hell hit me, anyway? And what are *you* doing here?"

Antonia explained as Win stood up, dusted himself off, and regained his composure. "Well, then, thanks, Antonia," he said. "*And* Nike." He gave the dog an awkward pat on the shoulder. "I suppose I'd better report this to the campus cops. If some crazed fraternity brother has escaped his keepers, they'll want to know about it."

It wasn't until she and Nike were back in the apartment that Antonia realized she hadn't told Win about his assailant's previous appearance. Assuming, that is, that it *was* the same man she'd seen the night before. Just before she went to bed, Antonia added this to her mental list of "Things to Do Tomorrow for Sure."

The only other item on this list was something that had occurred to her on the walk back from campus: "Go Talk to Ariadne's Family."

6

The Labyrinth

THE TWO-BUS, FORTY-FIVE-MINUTE RIDE THROUGH
busy streets to the north side of the city had, temporarily,
the effect Antonia had hoped for. It gave her the illusion
of going somewhere, of doing something. By way of ration-
alizing this rather quixotic foray into alien territory, she
kept reminding herself that she had, after all, gotten a bit
of information out of Bennie Thompson that he had with-
held from Caracci's men. For some reason he had trusted
her more than he had the police. Well, perhaps Ariadne's
family would feel the same way. She clung to the thought.

Once she was off the bus, the alienness of the district
became more and more oppressive. She moved through a
welter of blowing newspapers and junk-food wrappers.
Most of the shop signs she passed were in Greek: *TAVER-
NA, ARTOPOEION, FARMAKEION, TAVERNA*.

The address provided by the Student Directory turned
out to be neither house nor apartment building but a grimy
taverna. Faded Greek letters above the door identified it as
O LABYRINTHOS—The Labyrinth, an odd name for a
restaurant.

There was another sign overhanging the sidewalk at
right angles to the building, but it was so darkened by age
and weather that Antonia had difficulty making out the

subject. Painted apparently by an amateur of modest talents, it portrayed the Minotaur, monstrous offspring of Queen Pasiphaë of Crete and the white bull of Poseidon. Half bull and half—Antonia, startled, took a closer look and shivered. Was it mere technical incompetence, or had the unknown painter deliberately set the glowering bull's head on the body of a young child, narrow in the shoulders and chest and without any suggestion of musculature in the arms or thighs? The effect, far from being fearsome or even grotesque, was almost pathetic. The massive beast's head seemed a cruel burden for the childish body on which it rested. It reminded her horribly of a five-year-old hydrocephalic she had once glimpsed in a hospital corridor.

She stepped into The Labyrinth with some misgivings. The interior, however, was not particularly forbidding—nor particularly labyrinthine either. The proprietor was apparently one of those small restaurateurs whose entire imaginative capital is expended on the invention of a colorful name for their establishment, leaving them without the wherewithal to carry out the theme. In this instance, Antonia thought, it was probably just as well, if the sign outside was any indication.

The place was dark and dusty looking, but otherwise ordinary enough. Most of the bottles behind the bar were nearly full—ouzo, several varieties of *retsina, mavrodaphne,* and one incongruous fifth of Scotch. They stood shoulder to shoulder with a small army of *bríkia,* the little brass pots in which is brewed the powerful coffee of Greece and Turkey. The leatherette seats of the bar stools were cracked and torn, with bits of kapok protruding here and there like mocking tongues. The bar itself was stained and scarred, but it was still damp from a recent wiping.

No customers were in evidence, and Antonia was about to investigate a second room that opened off the first, where sounds of scrubbing seemed to indicate the presence of an employee. At this moment a beaded curtain rattled and a woman appeared behind the bar.

She was the kind of woman of whom one immediately and irresistibly thinks "she must have been beautiful once." Not, in this case, because she was very old—not more than forty-five, Antonia judged—and certainly not because she was aging gracefully. She was, in fact, fat and slovenly, but she had the indefinable air common to many fat women of never having cast off the habit of believing herself beautiful. It was in the way she carried the ugly fat on the splendid bones, it was in the arrow-straight Greek nose, it was in the dark eyes that were bitter and defiant now but must once have been invitingly bold.

"*Ti thélete, kyría?*" she said abruptly. "What you want?"

"Mrs. Pappas?" Taking a barely perceptible movement of the head as a grudging affirmative, Antonia forged ahead. "I'm Antonia Nielsen, one of Ariadne's professors at the university, and I'm a little concerned about her. I suppose you know that she's been missing for several days now, and—"

"You don' want nothing to drink?" The tone was belligerent.

"No, I only—that is, yes, I'll have a glass of wine. *Parakaló.*" Slightly mollified, the woman poured a glass of the most expensive *retsína* and pushed it a very few inches across the bar toward Antonia.

"Look, lady, I don' know nothing about my daughter. I never see her no more, she don' come home once a blue moon. I tol' the cop, I ain' seen her since February. What business it is to you, anyway?"

"Mrs. Pappas, I don't think you quite understand the situation. There's been a burglary at the University Museum where Ariadne works, and she's under suspicion."

The woman gave a contemptuous snort that jiggled her collection of chins. "She never do a thing like that."

So there is a spark of maternal loyalty buried under all that hostility, thought Antonia. Maybe I'm getting to her. "No," she said, "I quite agree. We all think . . ."

"She ain' got the guts," said the woman with finality.

So much for the maternal-loyalty angle. There was one other possibility, a long shot, but the best Antonia could do on the spur of the moment.

"She could go to prison, Mrs. Pappas. For a long time. And her chances of getting a job afterward . . ."

Far from her being shocked into a more cooperative attitude, Mrs. Pappas' tone grew uglier. "You mean she's gonna leave us on the lurch? *Kalá, kalá!*" And she burst into a torrent of Greek that Antonia couldn't follow in detail but that appeared to contain a high proportion of invective. It was clear that no help was to be expected from Ariadne's mother, and Antonia reached for her purse, intending to pay for her wine and leave. At a pause in the shrill tirade from behind the bar, she glanced up and realized that the last few words had been directed not at her but at a third person who was now standing in the doorway that connected the two rooms of the small *taverna*.

It was a young woman of twenty or so, dressed inelegantly in denim overalls and a headscarf. Her hands were abnormally clean and red, as if from hot sudsy water, and she was wiping them on a towel that protruded like a saucy tail from one hip pocket. She was evidently the source of the floor-scrubbing noises Antonia had noticed earlier. She listened dispassionately to the finale of Mrs. Pappas' tirade while she finished drying her hands. She had evidently witnessed such outbursts before and seemed neither startled nor embarrassed.

"*Sigá, mamá, sigá,*" she said when her mother paused for breath. "Professor Nielsen is only trying to help Ari." Then, turning to Antonia, "Miss Nielsen, I heard what you said and I appreciate your concern, but Mamá is a little upset and I don't think she cares to talk about it right now.

If you'd like to finish your wine, I'll go change my clothes and walk you back to the bus stop. I was going out anyway." And she ushered her mother gently but efficiently back through the bead curtain and up a narrow staircase that apparently led to the family living quarters on the second floor.

Antonia barely had time to finish the bitter *retsína* before the girl returned. The transformation was startling. Gone were the shapeless overalls and grimy bandanna. A simple knit dress, while leaving much to the imagination, hinted strongly that imagination was unlikely to exaggerate the facts. A great mane of black hair, freed from the scarf, fell in glossy masses over her shoulders. The huge dark eyes held a suggestion of mockery and more than a suggestion of determination, perhaps even ruthlessness if the need should arise. The mouth was good natured enough, wide and straight, the lips seeming barely to curve at all.

Yet despite the girl's almost melodramatic good looks, it was a small but incongruous detail that Antonia found most intriguing: a bracelet on the girl's left wrist, of simple design and exquisite workmanship. It was the only jewelry she wore, and perhaps the only piece she owned. It appeared to be made of solid gold.

As they left the *taverna*, Antonia involuntarily glanced up at the faded Minotaur sign. The girl's eyes, following her gaze, darkened as if at a painful memory. But her voice was matter-of-fact.

"We really ought to take that thing down, I suppose. My father painted it just before he died—that'd be almost twelve years now. He wasn't much of an artist, was he? It was kind of a family—joke, I guess you could call it. Mamá always hated it, though. When I was a kid I used to use it for a target: rocks in summer, snowballs in winter. The idea was to hit the bull's nose. I'd give myself ten points for hitting him square on the nose. The other kids would never play that game with me, though. I think they were a little scared of the sign, didn't understand what it meant. Or maybe they *did* understand. Anyway Ari always stopped me before I had a chance to zero in on that nose. She'd get real mad and make me quit." And she smiled with the amused tolerance of the grown woman of twenty for the ten-year-old tomboy she no longer recognizes as a part of herself.

"I take it that your father was something of a student of ancient Greece, then. I suppose that's where Ariadne got her interest in Classics?" It seemed innocuous enough as an opening gambit. Antonia had the impression that the girl was no more anxious than her mother to speculate about Ariadne's present predicament.

"I guess you could say that," the girl answered without enthusiasm. "It was sort of a bond between them, made them quite close in fact." Her tone was elaborately casual, almost bored, but again the little girl was visible behind the woman's self-possession. It wasn't hard to imagine the two sisters, one with a four- or five-year head start on capturing their father's attention by lisping bits of Euripides or Homer, the other feeling helpless anger as she realized she couldn't compete. Wrong tack again. What the hell was the *right* tack with this family, anyway? Antonia tried again.

"I'm sorry if I upset your mother again. I know having the police here must have been difficult enough. But I've been worried about Ariadne, and I thought possibly . . ."

"Don't worry, Professor, you didn't upset her. Nothing upsets Mamá. That's just the way she is about Ari." She paused and glanced at Antonia from under long, straight black eyebrows. She looked as if she were adding up a column of figures in her head.

"You see, Mamá has gotten it into her head that Ari is—well, prosperous. I've tried to explain to her that Ari isn't a professor yet, she's just in training, she doesn't have a real job. Mamá doesn't want to hear about all that. She's convinced herself that Ari has money somewhere that she's not sharing with us, and it nearly drives her mad. I'm afraid Mamá isn't very rational on the subject of money. I guess a lot of poor people aren't."

"Yes, but practically to wish her own daughter dead, in front of a total stranger! I couldn't follow everything she said in Greek, but . . ."

"Yes, Ma'am, that's just about what she was saying all right. My father used to say the Cretans are a violent people, and if Mamá's anything to go by I guess he was right. With her it's just talk, though. Mamá wouldn't actually *do* anything to anyone. Doing things isn't exactly her strong point." The wide straight lips curved in a bitter little smile that seemed to imply that no more family skeletons would be exhibited today.

"But it is true that you haven't seen or heard from Ariadne for some time? And you have no idea where she might have gone?"

"Oh, no, Mamá wasn't exaggerating that part. The last time Ari was here was in February, I think. She came one afternoon to leave a little money with me. She's afraid to mail it for fear Mamá will see the envelope before I do. Mamá isn't very reliable about money, like I said. Once in a while I even stop by Ari's office in the museum to see if she can spare us something. Anyway, that last time she stayed a couple of hours and then left, and we haven't seen her or talked to her since. She didn't say much while she was here either, just that she still thought she could finish up her degree by June and get a regular job in the fall. That's the only thing Mamá's interested in, of course, so that's about all Ari ever talks about when she's here. I really can't tell you any more than that."

"But you do understand what's happened—the burglary at the museum, and your sister's disappearance?"

"Yeah, I saw it on the evening news Friday and the cop explained when he was here." Then, with a smile that rather unpleasantly combined amusement and a kind of perverse satisfaction, she added, "Wherever she is, Ari'll be having a fit right now."

"Why do you say that?"

"You know how she is. She takes all that old stuff so seriously—jewelry and pots and statues, all that antiquity stuff. It'd kill her if any of it got ripped off—and out of her own museum too." Again Antonia heard an undertone of vindictive pleasure in the girl's voice. She seemed as indifferent to her sister's fate as her mother.

Her next words were an embarrassingly apt reply to Antonia's unspoken thought. "Don't get the idea I hate my sister. It isn't that. It's just that she's always been so high and mighty about our precious ancestors and all that. But I don't hate her. I even admire her in a way. At least she's gotten out of this, you have to give her that much. It's more than the rest of us have done." And she glanced bitterly around her at the decaying neighborhood of old apartment houses and dusty shops through which they were walking.

"You're not worried about Ariadne's just vanishing like this?"

"Ari," said the girl with conviction, "can take care of herself. Always has."

"Do you have any idea at all where she might have gone?"

Faced with the girl's unshakable nonchalance, Antonia was beginning to wonder whether she was indeed making mountains out of molehills.

"Not really. But she's done it before. She'll just take off on the bus for a few days, without telling anyone. To do some research, or something."

They had reached the bus stop, and Antonia's bus was approaching. The girl turned to her with an incongruous air of genteel formality, as if they were about to take leave of each other after sipping tea in a Victorian drawing room.

"Miss Nielsen," she said, extending her hand, "I do appreciate your taking such an interest in my sister. But I think perhaps you're exaggerating the seriousness of the situation just a little. I'm sure Ari's all right. It isn't likely we'll hear from her, but if we do I'll certainly let you know."

Across the street from the downtown stop where she had to change to the university bus stood a small pub. Antonia noticed it as she got off the downtown bus and decided to offer herself a drink as compensation for a wasted afternoon. Tomorrow's lecture notes could wait the extra half hour it would take to consume one beer and catch the next westbound bus.

Inside the pub the paneling was very dark and the lighting very dim. As she groped her way toward a booth, Antonia thought she could see a dartboard in one corner, though in that murky atmosphere it was hard to imagine how anyone could play a game without exposing his fellow patrons to the risk of grievous bodily injury.

Fortunately the proprietor's aspirations to authentic Englishness extended also to the serving of a very good imported ale. Antonia had consumed a delicious club sandwich and two ales and was congratulating herself on having salvaged this much at least from her futile expedition, when she saw them.

They had apparently just entered the pub, for the man was hanging their coats on the coatpole attached to the end of their booth, his activity effectively concealing his companion, who had already seated herself. But Antonia recognized him even though his back was turned to her, and when he sat down the woman's head, partially visible over the back of the booth, was familiar too.

Antonia shrank back into the corner of her own booth and hunched over her empty mug, hoping she was invisible in the semidarkness. They were sitting between her and the door. If she left now she would have to pass within a few feet of their booth and they would certainly see and recognize her. She was safe so long as they remained seated with their backs to her. But if she outwaited them there was a chance they would see her when they stood up to leave.

Her decision was hastened by the arrival of the waiter, inquiring whether she would have another mug. She nodded silently.

The girl must have waited at the same stop from which she had seen Antonia off and taken the next bus half an hour later. He would have come into town by the same bus that would take Antonia home, coming of course in the opposite direction. The point at which the two downtown bus routes intersected was an obvious place for a rendezvous, easily reached yet remote from the normal haunts of anyone who knew or cared about either him or her.

Until I went snooping, that is, thought Antonia, feeling both embarrassed and angry.

She made a conscious effort not to hear what they were saying. If it had not been superfluous the gesture would have been self-defeating, like trying not to think about falling asleep when you have insomnia. But fortunately they were sitting side by side, their heads very close together, and speaking very softly. Antonia couldn't hear their words but she couldn't help noticing that their conversation was filled with a certain emotional intensity she found disturbing.

Whatever its subject, the conversation was brief. The man rose abruptly after ten minutes, shrugged his coat on, and departed, leaving his mug half empty on the table. The woman stayed a few minutes longer, then she too stood up to leave.

For a split second, as she turned and reached for her coat, she faced Antonia. That she failed to see Antonia was due not so much to the dimness of the light as to the mental state she was in. That state was painfully obvious.

She had the look of an animal baffled of its prey. The hint of mockery in her dark eyes had hardened to a smoldering fury, the long straight lips were set in a cruel line. Even her hair, an aureole of leaping dark flames about her face, seemed to quiver with anger.

A woman scorned, thought Antonia with more aptness than originality. It looks as if Ariadne's sister has been, as they used to say, scorned. By my dear colleague Win Randolph.

Antonia gave the girl a five-minute head start to reduce the risk of running into her outside, then rose to leave. Halfway to the cashier's desk she nearly collided with a solid-looking figure in a topcoat. It was Caracci.

"What on earth are *you*—" they began in unison. They both laughed.

"Have you got a minute to talk, Miss Nielsen? I could even declare myself off duty and buy you a drink. I was planning to drown my own sorrows anyway."

"Sorry to hear you've got sorrows, Lieutenant, but yes, I'll join you. And thanks."

When he had ordered them a couple of mugs of ale, Antonia said, "This may be less of a coincidence than it looks, Lieutenant. I bet you had the same idea I had, and maybe the same luck. The Pappas women, am I right?"

"Just the mother this time. The daughter was out, so there wasn't anyone to interpret. The way the old girl was carrying on, though, I didn't really need anyone to translate her Greek."

Antonia gave him a sympathetic smile. "I know what you mean. I got exactly the same treatment." She didn't tell him that she had talked to Ariadne's sister, for fear of being drawn into revealing that she had later seen the girl with Win in this very tavern. She wanted more time to think about that, to try to find some innocuous explanation for their being together, before she mentioned it to anyone.

"It was a pretty feeble hope anyway, I suppose," Caracci said. "But I'm not making much progress with this Aegean Gold business and I guess I was grasping at straws." He sounded discouraged.

"Oh lord, the Gold!" Antonia exclaimed.

"Yeah, the Aegean—" Someone had corrected his pronunciation since their previous talk, she noticed.

"No, I mean—I hadn't made the connection until just now, but last night . . ." And she described the attack on Win outside the museum, and her own sighting of what might have been the same man the night before.

Caracci listened intently. By the time she finished, he was looking thoroughly disapproving.

"Are you telling me, Miss Nielsen, that you saw a colleague of yours get mugged last night, got your dog to chase the assailant away, and then calmly went home to bed and forgot the whole thing? That this happened in a place where you had previously noticed a suspicious individual, a place that had been the site of a well-publicized burglary a few days before? And it never occurred to you to mention any of this to the police?"

"Win was going to report it to the campus police. Neither of us associated the attack on him with the break-in at the museum. Surely whoever did that wouldn't be so stupid as to hang around the scene of the crime the next two nights? Win and I both assumed that it was some student, probably drunk, doing one of the silly and in-comprehensible things students do under the combined influence of alcohol and spring fever. We thought of it as a *campus* problem, not a matter for the metropolitan police. I also assumed that after Win talked to the campus cops they would pass on to you anything they thought you should know."

"Yeah, they're supposed to." Caracci's moment of in-dignation seemed to have passed. "Students and spring and chemicals, that's their kind of problem usually. You think maybe this weather's been getting to the kids?"

"I wouldn't be surprised. I know it's been getting to *me*. Friday especially, I was so busy thinking about all the places I'd rather be and the things I'd rather be doing, I could hardly teach. Of course, I stopped short of mugging my colleagues or robbing museums. Lousy lectures are about the closest I ever get to antisocial behavior traceable to spring fever."

"I never thought you liberated professional types would get anything as old-fashioned as spring fever," Caracci grinned. "That's kind of encouraging, in a way."

"Sure we do." Antonia smiled back. "Only of course with us it takes more sophisticated forms. I, for example, was having fantasies about exploring Crete, maybe discov-ering a whole new Minoan site. Nothing so reactionary as a handsome man on a white horse or a white Honda. That's not permitted to us liberated professional types."

They both laughed, and the subject of the Saturday Night Skulker did not arise again.

7

The Tower

FROM THE NORTHEAST CORNER OF THE OLD BUILD-
ing that housed the University Museum rose a tower. The
aesthetic intentions of the Victorian architect who had
perpetrated this tower were the subject of endless conjec-
ture and controversy among the wittier elements of the
academic community.

There was the Spanish-mission bell tower faction, the
Renaissance campanile faction, and the Marxist-oriented
faction, which held that the thing was patterned after the
smokestacks of a nineteenth-century textile mill. There was
even a lunatic fringe that maintained the designer drew his
inspiration from a prophetic dream of a rocket gantry.

Whatever its origins, the tower's present function was
prosaic enough. Except for its topmost story, it was occupied by the offices of several of the museum's administra-
tive staff. They were the more junior members, expected
to take whatever was offered in the way of office space.
The tower was well known to be underheated, drafty, and
remote from the more active sectors of the museum. It
also lacked an elevator. It was nobody's idea of prime office
space.

There had been a period, however, just before the new
Humanities Building was constructed, when every broom

closet and telephone booth on campus was pressed into service as offices for the humanities faculty. It was a time they all remembered with distaste, a time of fragmented departments and long walks to class in every weather.

It was at this unlamented period that Win Randolph and another classicist had drawn the top floor of the museum tower. His colleague had departed from the university just before the completion of the Humanities Building, leaving Win in sole possession of the dim, low-ceilinged, vaguely medieval-looking room. When the call at last went forth for the scattered humanities departments to reassemble themselves in their new cement-block cubicles, Win refused to move. Five years later he was still holding undisputed sway over the only faculty office on campus with diamond-paned casement windows.

Not surprisingly, a sizable body of legend had grown up around Randolph's Tower. The gist of it was that the tower room regularly witnessed scenes of riotous living unheard of in the antiseptic cubicles of the new Humanities Building. A battered steel storage cabinet was said to house a respectable array of wines and spirits. A humble single-burner hotplate was apotheosized, on the lips of the legend-makers, into the central element of elaborate and exotic tea ceremonies.

But it was the sagging couch in one of the dimmer corners of the room that inspired the juiciest episodes in the Legend of the Tower.

The legend, at this point, split into two distinct branches. According to the first, Win had more than once spent the night on this couch (alone), after heated marital disputes that terminated in his being locked out of the house by Gillian.

The second branch was the more popular. It stressed, predictably enough, the seduction of coeds in numbers that varied radically from source to source. This subdivision of the legend was especially rich in variants, some versions insisting, for example, that Win's attentions were not confined exclusively to students but occasionally extended to his female colleagues on the faculty.

Knowing Win better than most of his colleagues did, Antonia had always been quite sure that the juicier segments of the legend were apocryphal. That he occasionally offered a cup of coffee to a student was of course quite possible. And—though all-night bouts of hard work at his desk were hardly Win's style—it was even conceivable that he had once or twice fallen asleep on the notorious couch after working late and spent the night there rather than drag himself home.

But Win Randolph as wholesale seducer, whether of coeds or colleagues, in towers or elsewhere—this aspect of the legend she had never taken seriously. Questions of moral rectitude and husbandly devotion aside, he was simply not daring enough. But now, as she sat curled up on her sofa with a sheaf of half-read lecture notes in her lap, Antonia wondered.

By the time she reached home she had decided that her instinctive reaction to the interlude in the pub had been overhasty. She had always been a skeptic on the question of intuition, feminine or otherwise, and she saw no reason to become a true believer at this late date. It made no sense to conclude from one ambiguous incident that Win Randolph was having an affair with a girl half his age.

On the other hand, if the confrontation in the pub had not been an amorous adventure—or the terminal episode of one—then what *had* they been doing there together? The sister, in conversation with Antonia, had put on an elaborate show of nonchalance concerning Ariadne's whereabouts. Was it possible that she was more disturbed by her sister's disappearance than she had admitted, and that she had enlisted Win's help in trying to locate her? But why should she be willing to talk to Win and not to Antonia? And what could Win have said to make the girl so furiously angry, if they were discussing her missing sister?

Reluctantly, Antonia returned to the erotic interpretation of the scene in the pub. Intuitive it might be, and distasteful it certainly was, but it seemed to fit the few known facts better than any other she could think of.

What about Gillian's suspicions concerning Ariadne? Two nights ago Antonia had thought them ridiculous and a little pathetic. Had poor Gillian been right, then, or half-right, barking (unkind metaphor) at the wrong branch of the right tree?

Antonia turned with relief to the notes, skimming for continuity through last month's material before settling down to polish tomorrow's lecture: *Euripides*, she read, *youngest of three great Athenian tragedians. B. during wars with Persia, d. during wars with Sparta. Wrote 92 plays of which 19 extant plus frgs. Knowledge of lost plays still increasing: papyri. . . .*

Monday morning was no worse than other Monday mornings. The usual assortment of students, secretaries, and colleagues paraded in and out of Antonia's office, on the usual errands: I can't understand why I got a B-minus on this exam . . . would you mind signing this . . . have you seen Smedley's article in AJP . . .

The burglary seemed to be losing steam already as a topic of conversation.

Then, just as Antonia was preparing to leave for lunch, Win stuck his head in the door. She had been thankful for his nonappearance during the morning, not knowing how she would react when they did meet. The decision was now taken out of her hands, temporarily at least.

"Thanks again for your deed of derring-do the other night," Win began. "Yours and Nike's, that is. I reported our little fracas to the campus cops, by the way. They seemed less impressed with the peril to my person than I could have wished, but they did promise to look into it. At least it'll keep them constructively occupied and out of trouble for a few days."

The tone of sardonic condescension toward all members of the university community below the rank of full professor was typical of Win Randolph. But beneath the banter Antonia thought she detected a weariness, a kind of heaviness, that was not at all typical. He looked, for once, his full forty-two years, perhaps even a bit more. The battered tweed jacket and rumpled hair failed, this morning, to make him look his usual boyish twenty-five.

"Win," Antonia began abruptly, "is Gillian all right?"

He sank into the steel-and-plastic armchair that was the cubicle's only concession to hospitality. "I don't know," he said unhappily. "She *seems* calm enough now—almost too calm, I'm afraid. Feels she made a fool of herself Friday night, of course."

Antonia made a vague murmur.

"The—other time," he continued with an effort, "she was calm too, after the initial blowup. And yet a few hours later she—but you were there. Of course that was a more violent explosion. . . ."

Indeed it had been. Although the blond coed had showed a quite saintly forbearance after they pulled Gillian off her, it was obvious that the girl had passed through a few moments of stark terror, of genuine—and quite justi-fied—fear for her life. Though not athletic, Gillian was tall and by no means fragile, and she had the added strength of temporary insanity, or what looked a lot like it.

"Which could mean," Win was saying, "one of two things. Either this was a milder . . . attack, or whatever you want to call it—or else it was somehow dammed up before it ran its full course. In which case there may be, God help us, more to come." He stood up painfully. "I'd better be getting home. I may be overreacting, but I'm not really sure I should leave her alone."

He had reached the door. In desperation, Antonia blurted out the question there seemed to be no tactful way of introducing at such a moment.

"Win, before you leave, I—I saw you yesterday talking to Ariadne's sister. I wouldn't have mentioned it except —did you get anything out of her? I went to see her too, and Ariadne might have been a total stranger for all the girl would tell me about her."

Win's voice, as he turned back from the door again, held a trace of annoyance.

"As a matter of fact, Antonia, we weren't discussing Ariadne. She asked me to meet her there to talk over a— personal matter."

Antonia must have looked as embarrassed as she felt, because Win hastily went on.

"Now hold on, Antonia, I didn't mean all *that* personal. The fact is, the wretched girl has been trying to get me to 'exercise some influence,' as she puts it, to get her a job here—preferably as secretary to one of our larger departments. She started in on me the first time we ever met—at Ariadne's desk in the museum. I'd stopped by to return a couple of chapters of her dissertation, as I often do. Since we both work in the same building, it's more convenient. Anyway, her sister was there that day, looking— well, you saw the way she looks. She seemed to take a shine to me. 'Ari's told me so much about you, Professor Randolph,' et cetera. Corny as hell, and of course I didn't fall for it. Not for the first two or three minutes, at least. Next thing I knew, we were having a drink in that same pub where you saw us yesterday, and I was on the brink of earning—at long last—my hitherto undeserved reputation as Lothario-in-residence."

"Seems a lot of trouble to go to for a typing job," Antonia observed skeptically.

"You don't understand, Antonia. Neither did I, for that matter, not at first. But yesterday—after I'd made it clear that I don't intend to do any more for her—she lost her cool for a few minutes and let me see what she's really after."

"And that is?"

"I hardly know how to put it to one of your enlightened views, Antonia, without giving offense. Her object, in its archaic simplicity and its Neanderthal crudeness, is matrimony."

Antonia refused to rise to the bait. She was remembering the girl's bitter words at the bus stop the day before. *Ari's gotten out of this. It's more than the rest of us have done.* And the occasional little lapses into what she probably thought of as more refined speech: *Mamá doesn't care to talk about it. I do appreciate your interest. . . .* And that beautiful gold bracelet that must have cost several weeks' salary. If she *had* a salary.

"Matrimony," Win went on, "not of course to me, but to one of the dozens of eligible men who would be hanging around her typewriter all day. A graduate student, an instructor . . . who knows? Maybe even one of the lesser deans. A man with a future. That, Antonia, is what was at stake, not a mere 'typing job,' as you so uncharitably put it."

What was at stake was a whole new life, thought Antonia, remembering the grimy *taverna*. Comfort, security, what used to be called respectability. To someone starting from where the Pappas family had, those things could seem all-important, well worth selling your looks for. Not a very dignified way "out of this," but a lot faster and easier than getting a Ph.D. in nuclear physics, as the feminists would have preferred her to. Or even classical Greek. That had been Ariadne's way. This girl was trying to do it in hers, and Antonia was not disposed to pass judgment on her. But her method was far from subtle—surely trying to seduce Win Randolph was overkill. He would have given her some sort of recommendation for the asking, in all probability. Apparently she hadn't realized that, had imagined the price of entry was higher than it actually was.

"But why yesterday in particular?"

"She'd gotten the idea, from television and perhaps also from that detective, that the university regards her sister as a prime suspect in the museum burglary. She was terrified that this would compromise her job application, here and everywhere else. Kept saying, 'Who would ever trust me, after this?'"

"What did you tell her?"

"I tried to convince her that her precious application was okay—in actual fact, I suspect it's lying dead in a file somewhere—but she didn't let up. Kept demanding that I talk to someone, make more phone calls, *do* something. Finally I couldn't take any more and told her there was nothing more I could or would do for her. Period. Rather anticlimactic, isn't it, after what you probably imagined you saw yesterday?"

"I'm sorry, Win. You know I didn't mean to spy."

"No, of course not. No harm done. I'll see you tomorrow—or Wednesday more likely. I haven't any classes tomorrow, and I may just loll about the house. Take care."

Watching him go, Antonia remembered the fury on the girl's face. Could the meeting have been as innocent as Win implied?

When Antonia returned from lunch an hour later, Caracci was waiting outside her office, his stocky business-suited figure incongruous among the leggy jean-clad students who hurried past him in the narrow corridor.

She smiled at him. "Didn't expect to see you again so soon, Lieutenant. I'm afraid I haven't any more prowlers, skulkers, or lurkers up my sleeve, if that's what you're hoping for." It was a relief no longer to have any clandestine trysts between Ariadne's sister and dissertation director up her sleeve, either. She unlocked the door and he followed her into the office, where he settled without invitation into the one spare chair.

"Your first one hasn't done much for us so far, Miss Nielsen. We had a man watching the museum last night, and there was nothing to watch. But that's not what I've come about. No further word on the Pappas girl, I suppose." He didn't bother to make it sound like a question, but Antonia shook her head anyway.

"But what I really wanted to talk to you about was this Thompson kid. Bennie Thompson."

"I see." She didn't, but from the not very subtle hints Bennie had dropped concerning his relationship with Caracci, she had a fair idea what to expect.

"I wonder if you do, Miss Nielsen. He finally got around to calling me last night. He says he talked to you Saturday and you were—sympathetic, I think was the word he used. And that's what worries me."

"Now I'm afraid I *don't* see, Lieutenant. You're telling me I shouldn't be sympathetic to Bennie Thompson? I should have thought that was my own business, not a matter for police investigation."

"Ordinarily it would be your business, of course. But Bennie isn't exactly an ordinary boy, and I want to be sure you understand what you're getting into."

"I wasn't aware that I was 'getting into' anything, Lieutenant. I've talked to Bennie exactly once, for perhaps an hour. We were both concerned about Ariadne Pappas, who happens to be a mutual friend and who hasn't been seen or heard from for something like four—"

"I know, I know," Caracci cut her short. "And maybe that's all it is, concern for his friend. But I think you should also be aware that—for my money, anyway—Bennie is a prime suspect in this theft business. Even more to the point, he also happens to be a former drug addict."

"But why is that so much to the point, Lieutenant? He's doing very well for himself now, as far as I can see. He's got a steady job, he works hard, he's said to be very reliable—what more could you ask?"

"Nothing—except for the fact that a very valuable collection of objects is missing from his place of employment. Objects that should have been locked up in a safe, but were somehow left lying around loose like pencils and paperclips that particular night. Plus the fact that he just happened to be at the opposite end of the building and two floors up when all that gold was taken. Coincidence? Bad luck? We don't know yet, Miss Nielsen, but we intend to find out."

"I'm sorry, Lieutenant, but to my untutored ear that doesn't exactly sound like an airtight case against the boy."

"I'm not making a case against him, Miss Nielsen. I'm concerned about you, that's all. Even if Bennie had nothing to do with the break-in at the museum, he could be a dangerous friend. I just wanted you to know that. What you do about it is your business, as you say."

"Thanks, Lieutenant. I'll try not to do anything rash. But the one I'm concerned about is Ariadne. She's been gone for almost four days now. Isn't there something you can do?"

"Can't do much more than I have, Miss Nielsen. She

isn't officially missing, of course—and with a family like hers she isn't likely to be, either. She could be gone four years, let alone four days, and I doubt *they'd* report it."

Her own frustrating encounter with Ariadne's mother and sister still fresh in her mind, Antonia could only agree, silently and glumly, with this assessment of the Pappas family's solidarity.

"In other words, if I want to find Ariadne Pappas I can go and look for her myself." Antonia knew she was being unduly sharp with Caracci, but his imperturbable coolness concerning her student was getting on her nerves.

"No, Ma'am, I wasn't suggesting that. Like I said, we've done everything we can. I doubt you'd have any better luck tracing her on your own—and maybe you don't have quite the resources we have." His voice was calm, without a trace of either condescension or resentment. Unreasonably, Antonia felt her own annoyance increase.

"Sorry, Lieutenant," she said then, in what she hoped was a more cordial tone. "I didn't mean to question your procedures. But I *am* worried about the girl. She's extremely competent academically, but in other ways she gives such an impression of friendlessness, of vulnerability."

"I understand your concern, Ma'am. But if Miss Pappas shows up at her mother's place, or her own apartment, or any hospital in the city, we'll know about it. Most likely, though, she'll just turn up right here at the university in a day or two and wonder what all the fuss is about. Assuming she wasn't involved in the theft. Happens all the time, believe me."

It was only after he had left that the implication of the phrase came home to her. *Any hospital in the city. If she shows up at any hospital in the city, we'll know about it.*

8

Another Labyrinth

THIS DISTURBING TRAIN OF THOUGHT WAS INTER-
rupted by the precipitous entrance of Barry Greenfield.
He bounded into Antonia's office unannounced, pointed
an accusing forefinger at her nose, and demanded, "Where
were *you*, Madam, on the evening of Saturday, April seventh, between the hours of eight and eleven? Or was it the
eighth? Anyway, where the hell were you?"

"Saturday," she said thoughtfully. "Ah, yes, Saturday.
That was the night I spent with Prince Charles. Or was
it—no, definitely the prince. Robert Redford was the Saturday *before*."

Barry assumed a reproachful expression and flopped
into the vacant chair. "Really, Antonia," he said, "your
levity is most unseemly. It was a serious question. Couched,
it may be, in the typically effervescent Greenfield style, but
a serious question nonetheless. You may possibly recall,"
he added severely, "that I invited you to dinner."

"Oh," she said in a small voice. "Yes. You did, didn't
you."

She remembered now. When he had returned her and
her bike to her apartment Friday afternoon, he had said
something about broiling a steak Saturday for himself and

Marsha—his latest conquest among the graduate students —and letting Antonia have the bones to gnaw.

Her brief moment of contrition, however, was cut short by a cackle of delighted laughter from Barry.

"Never mind, old girl. The expression on your face was compensation enough for one cold T-bone that Marsha and I had to finish up for you. It was rare—your expression, that is, not the steak, which was slightly overdone. Associate Professor Antonia Nielsen, M.A., Ph.D., looking like a kitten that's just been caught in an indiscretion on the living room carpet."

"I withdraw," retorted Antonia, "any apology that may have been implied or inferred."

"No, no, my child, you mustn't apologize. We all have these occasional . . ."

"Oh do shut up, Barry." This was the note on which their horseplay habitually ended, and implied no rancor on either side.

An assistant professor of English in his second year of teaching at the university, Barry Greenfield was already something of an *enfant terrible* on the faculty. Upon emerging from the cocoon of graduate school, well-deserved Ph.D. in hand, he had looked around, taken a deep breath, and plunged with exuberance into the life so eloquently chronicled in the pages of *Playboy* and *Penthouse*.

In particular, having read somewhere that a man's smile is one of the first things a woman notices, he had practiced for weeks to acquire a serviceable basic vocabulary of smiles: the Smile Friendly, the Smile Confiding, the Smile Rueful, the Smile Invitational, and (most essential) the Smile Intimate. What his best friends never had the heart to tell him was that the entire repertoire resembled nothing so much as a set of variations on the Grin Boyish.

No matter—by whatever name, the Greenfield smile worked. It stirred in numerous female undergraduates a sudden fascination with the intricacies of the eighteenth-century English novel. It inspired in certain normally morose departmental secretaries a cheerful willingness to please that was downright frightening. And it had earned him a long series of triumphant conquests among the women graduate students.

This postponed adolescence should have been annoying in a man almost thirty, but somehow in Barry's case it wasn't. He had been very busy and very poor during the years when he should have been getting all this out of his system. It seemed to Antonia no more than fair that he should have his fling now, more particularly since he seemed to be causing little grief and a good deal of happiness. He had an amazing knack of leaving few broken hearts, no hard feelings, and a lot of lasting friendships in his wake. Antonia, who was two years older than Barry, had often told him that she was dying to see what he would be like when he grew up. His usual reply was that she would just have to wait and see because he wasn't ready for her yet.

In reality, of course, it was neither his repartee nor the famous smile that attracted Antonia to him. For Barry also possessed certain other qualities, rarely extolled in the pages of *Playboy*, that had made them close friends and that (if the truth were known) accounted for most of his success with women. He was a generous and perceptive man who cared about people he found interesting. Some of these people were women, and Antonia was one of them.

"All right," Barry sighed now, "I abandon the interrogation. But we *were* a bit concerned, especially after we began to hear those rumors about the Saturday Night Skulker. Couldn't reach you by phone, either."

"That's because I'd unplugged it. I'd had a couple of

rather trying days and I needed to get away from it all for a while." And she gave a brief account of her first conversation with Caracci, the Randolphs' dinner, and her talk with Bennie Thompson.

"By the time Bennie left," she concluded, "my brain was beginning to crumble around the edges. Ariadne stealing Aegean Gold, Ariadne seducing her thesis director, Ariadne lurking about the museum at three in the morning. . . . I wrestled with all that for a while, trying to make some sense out of it, and then I just forced myself to stop thinking about it for the rest of the evening. I am sorry about your dinner, though."

"Doesn't matter. But this student of yours—she is an enigma, isn't she? Marsha roomed with her, you know, for a short time last year. And from what she's said, Ariadne certainly didn't strike me as the type to get herself involved in burglary and adultery and—well, whatever it is that's going on around here. Whatever type *that* may be."

"I think we can dismiss burglary and adultery from serious consideration. It's this vanishing act that has me worried. But I seem to be the only one who finds it odd. The police, her own family, even Win—they all seem to think there's nothing out of the ordinary in her going off for a few days without telling anyone."

"There's the guard, of course—what's his name? *He* doesn't feel it's so ordinary. Wasn't that why he came to you on Saturday?"

"Bennie Thompson. Well, he *may* be worried about Ariadne, among other things. But that gets us into the question of *his* motives." Reluctantly, wondering if she were betraying some sort of trust, she told Barry about the boy's unsavory past and Caracci's distrust of him.

"But even if he is trying—rather clumsily, it seems to me—to make the girl look suspicious, I doubt he made up that story out of whole cloth. When she comes back, it'll be her word against his, and from what you say I gather Bennie's word doesn't carry a whole lot of weight with the cops." Barry paused. "And that may be your best lead right there, Antonia."

"What do you mean?"

"This office or workroom or whatever it is in the museum. The room where Bennie says Ariadne has been spending her nights, and where the theft occurred, as I understand it."

"What about it? The police have been over it pretty carefully, I assume."

"Yes, but not with Ariadne in mind. They were looking for evidence in connection with the burglary. Now from what you and Marsha have told me about this girl, I get the impression that her work is the most important thing in her life."

"The only important thing, as far as I can see."

"Right. Well then, doesn't it stand to reason that if she's behaving oddly—oddly for *her*, that is—the reason may have something to do with her work? Not her family or her friends, who don't seem to be extremely significant figures in her life, not even the museum theft, but the one thing that *does* matter to her. Her work."

"In other words, something may have gone wrong with her dissertation." Antonia sounded unconvinced. "It's possible, I suppose. And that probably would be enough to make her act erratically for a while. But surely Win would have said something if it were only the dissertation. He knows I've been worrying about her."

"But what if it isn't her dissertation?"

"But there isn't anything else it could be. The dissertation *is* her work right now."

"She must have job applications outstanding, probably dozens of them."

"Well, yes, but . . ."

"And what about this project she's working on at the museum? What is it they're doing, sorting papyri or something? What if Ariadne has accidentally smashed up an irreplaceable papyrus and aroused the wrath of Miss Lilly?"

"Oh, Barry, for God's sake be serious."

"But I am serious. All right, granted she probably hasn't smashed up any significant quantity of papyrus or dropped much red-figure crockery. My point is, this girl is involved—professionally involved—in more than just a doctoral dissertation. She has a temporary job now; she's looking for a permanent one for next September. That's two potential sources of trouble right there. You know what the academic marketplace is like these days, Antonia, we all do. Every graduate student and untenured faculty member in the country gets the shakes at the very mention of the word *job*."

"Yes, I suppose you're right," Antonia said thoughtfully. "And I suppose it's even possible that she's gone stale on the dissertation and turned to something else for a while. I've known graduate students to do that occasionally."

"You mean the old term paper on which one of us scribbled 'with additional research and revisions, this could be a publishable article'?"

"Something like that. Ariadne's the kind who would rather turn to a new project than sit and stare doggedly at something she's too sick of to work at any longer."

"So there's a third possibility for you. Maybe she's just gone somewhere for a few days to do that additional research. Well, my dear, now that I've shed light into the dark places, unraveled the tangled skein, and poured oil upon the troubled waters of your soul, that'll be fifty dollars. Standard consultation fee, rates upon request."

"Your metaphors," Antonia observed tartly, "lack distinction."

When he was gone, though, she admitted to herself that some of his ideas weren't bad.

She did not imagine that he had hit upon the correct explanation of Ariadne's disappearance. The girl might or might not have gone off to do research in another library. She might or might not have suffered a setback in her search for a permanent position, might or might not have had some kind of falling out with her superiors at the museum. That was all speculation.

What mattered was the principle behind the speculation. The principle was, in fact, annoyingly obvious now that Barry had called it to her attention. Look at the girl's work, he had said, look at her professional life. Well, that was precisely what she was going to do. The same restlessness that had led her to The Labyrinth, and her encounter with Ariadne's mother and sister, came over her again.

The police presumably had been through the girl's desk in the museum. But how much would Caracci and his men understand of what they were looking at? Scholarly notes, the rough draft of a research paper, Xeroxed texts in ancient languages with marginal scribbles—what sense could a detective be expected to make of such things?

She glanced at her watch. Four-thirty already. By the time she could get to the museum, it would be within a few minutes of closing. It would have to wait until tomorrow. She packed her briefcase and drove home, feeling vaguely cheated.

She reached her apartment building and rode up in the elevator with a growing sense of oppression and frustration that the closeness of the tiny elevator did nothing to relieve. The feeling was still with her when she stepped out into her own corridor and walked the few yards to her apartment door. But as she groped in her coat pocket for the door key, she had a sudden inspiration. For a few seconds she gazed speculatively at the spot beside the door where Bennie had been lying in wait for her two days ago. Then she rushed into the apartment, brushed past Nike's welcoming gambols, and headed for the bedroom phone.

The evening passed quickly. The pressures and tensions of the past few days seemed to gather themselves into a bundle of energies and impulses that proceeded to burst forth in all sorts of whimsical directions, like a cluster of skyrockets. It first occurred to her that part of her depressed mood might be attributable to sheer hunger, inasmuch as she had not eaten a really substantial meal in almost three days. So she cooked herself an elaborate stew, with gourmet scraps for Nike and several quarts left over to freeze for some future dinner party.

Thus fortified, she went through her four rooms like the Avenging Angel of Good Housekeeping, dusting off, straightening up, putting away, and throwing out. Nike looked on with an air compounded of bewilderment and disapproval. Under normal circumstances, Antonia's philosophy on the subject was of the once-a-month-if-I-happen-to-think-of-it variety, a philosophy that perfectly coincided with Nike's refined distaste for dust in the air and for the removal of familiar and beloved objects from one place to another. A well-seasoned clutter was Nike's preferred lifestyle. Now, sensing that circumstances were *not* normal, the dog withdrew to a secluded corner of the bathroom until such time as her associate should return to a more rational view of things.

At ten o'clock Antonia flopped into an armchair expecting to feel pleasantly tired. Finding, however, that she was as restless as before, she evicted Nike from the bathroom and treated herself to a steamy shower. But there was still half an hour to kill. So she corralled the dog and spent the remaining time grooming her, a process that relaxed them both. Nike adored being combed. Her brown-velvet eyes would grow dreamy and remote and she would lean blissfully into the comb, sunk in reveries of her ancestors hunting gazelles along the Nile five thousand years ago.

The ecstasy came to an abrupt end at the stroke of eleven, however. Antonia tossed the comb aside, gave the big Afghan a dismissive whack on the rump, and headed for the coat closet. Nike, with a sigh of regret, shook herself out of her trance and padded hopefully after. Briefly, Antonia considered taking her along, then decided against it. Where she was going, a single wave of that lovely plumed tail might be catastrophic. So she closed the apartment door regretfully but firmly in Nike's face. With a reproachful sigh the dog took up her regular post just inside the door. It had been, from her point of view, a most unorthodox evening.

Antonia had entertained vague apprehensions of staggering blindly through the darkened grounds of the museum, collecting scratches from the shrubbery and perhaps a twisted ankle or two. The reality turned out to be a good deal less Gothic.

The approach to the main façade of the museum complex was through a small garden surrounding a rectangular reflecting pool. Four brick walkways bordered by low hedges led through the garden and up two flights of stairs to the main entrance. Opportunities for tumbling into the pool, stumbling into the hedges, or turning an ankle on the stairs were severely limited, however, inasmuch as the entire area was most efficiently illuminated by a dozen powerful spotlights concealed in the shrubbery and under the eaves of the building itself.

She negotiated the little garden without difficulty but stopped at the foot of the steps that led up to the main entrance. In her excitement, she now realized, she had neglected to tell Bennie where to meet her. The wide front portal, dramatically lighted as it was, looked altogether too public for the sort of cloak-and-dagger operation she had in mind. Oh, come off it, Nielsen, she told herself, and started up the steps.

Somewhere behind her and to her right she heard a low grating sound. Startled, she whirled around and saw a long ribbon of light in the darkest section of the wing enclosing that side of the courtyard. The ribbon slowly widened until it assumed the dimensions of a doorway, most of which was filled by a tall, gangling silhouette. The silhouette hissed her name and beckoned with one hand while holding the door open with the other. She had to take it on faith that the dark shape was Bennie, at least until she was so close to him that escape would have been impossible if it had turned out to be someone more sinister.

It was Bennie, of course. But he yanked her almost violently into the building, and closed and locked the door behind them with such nervous intensity that Antonia was reminded of Caracci's warning not to trust the boy too far. A bit late to be thinking of that, she told herself, now that you've got yourself locked up in an unfamiliar building with him in the middle of the night.

His voice was gruff as he said, "Sorry, Professor. But they got this place staked out, y'know, and I was afraid . . ."

"They've what? You mean there are cops out there?"

"Yeah, sure. I don't know what they figure is gonna happen around here *now*, but I told you they didn't trust me. Or maybe they think Ari might come sneaking back in the dark of the moon or something. Anyway, they're out there all right, been there ever since the break-in."

"Well, I suppose there's nothing we can do about it now. If they saw me come in and if they come in after us, we'll just have to tell them the truth and hope they'll buy it. Meanwhile, I may as well get to work. Which way to the scene of the crime?"

Her flippant tone and optimistic mood were dampened somewhat by the long trek through the museum's subterranean corridors. The exhibition floors above had been renovated and modernized several times in the institution's history, in accordance with changing tastes and notions about the proper display of art objects and ancient artifacts. Down here, however, little had changed in the hundred years the museum had been in existence. The light, which emanated from bare bulbs hanging at widely spaced intervals from the low ceilings, was dimmer than it had been outside. The ceilings themselves were a welter of pipes and heating ducts that writhed over, under, and around one another. Periodically a group of them would go snaking off down a side corridor and lose themselves in the gloom.

The walls had been painted, at some remote period, in an institutional cream color that had not aged gracefully. By now it resembled dirty vanilla pudding. Set into the walls were equally unappetizing metal doors with placards that flashed past in the half-light as Bennie hurried her along. She made out a few of them: Associate Curator of Sculpture, Publications Director, Reproductions Department, Librarian . . .

"Here we are," said Bennie, pulling up outside a door indistinguishable from the others. In the eerie silence his voice sounded unnaturally loud. "Workroom," announced the placard noncommittally. Bennie swung the door open and switched on a bank of fluorescent lights overhead.

"That's Ari's desk over there," he said abruptly. Antonia had the impression that he wanted to dissociate himself as much as possible from her rather unorthodox investigation. A bit late for that, she thought again, though understandable.

"Look, you go and make your rounds or whatever, and I'll do what I can here. Could you come back in half an hour or so and escort me out? I'm not sure I could find that door again, in this heavy twilight."

"Yeah, they got real energy-conscious around here a couple years ago. Okay, you look around in here and I'll come back in about a half hour. Happy hunting, Professor," he added. "I dunno what you figure on finding in here, but between you and the fuzz ain't none of us gonna have no secrets left round here." He laughed sardonically and left, closing the door of the workroom behind him. Antonia could hear his steps for some time. They echoed with abnormal loudness in the deserted building, so that she could follow his progress down the long corridor and around some unseen corner. Finally they died away and she turned to the room.

It was only slightly less depressing than the corridors. Same dirty-vanilla walls, same snaky-looking tangle of pipes infesting the ceiling. But the workroom at least looked inhabited, looked as if purposeful human activities were regularly carried on in it. Each of its four corners was occupied by a large battered desk, one of which Bennie had pointed out as belonging to Ariadne.

Most of the rest of the room was taken up by a huge worktable that appeared to have been beaten with chains and subsequently bathed in acid, several centuries ago. Scratched, scarred, dented, and stained though it was, it stood solid and massive, looking as if nothing short of dynamite could move it. The impression of permanence and indispensability was enhanced by the litter of manuals, papers, and implements that covered most of its surface.

There were bottles of adhesive, fixative, varnish, and paint with their attendant brushes and wipe rags.

But most interesting to Antonia was a little army of white cards propped vertically in Lucite holders and ranged in two neat rows in the middle of the great worktable. Nearby lay a stack of blank cards, an array of lettering pens, and an assortment of India ink bottles.

She stooped a little to read the finished cards.

Gold bowl with incised linear decoration, 2800–2500 B.C. ? Euboea. 9 cm high.

Silver cup with two handles, 19th c. B.C. Gournia. 8 cm high.

Golden pendant with appliqué and granulated decoration of two hornets and honeycomb. 17th c. B.C. Mallia. 4.6 cm high.

Gold-hilted dagger, bronze blade with inlay of hunting leopards, 15th c. B.C. Pylos. 32 cm long.

Bronze dagger blade (hilt lost) with gold. silver, and niello inlay of a lion hunt, 16th c. B.C. Shaft Grave V, Mycenae. 23.8 cm long.

Gold 'tea-cup' with embossed double-spiral decoration and ribbon handle, 15th c. B.C. Knossos. 3.7 cm high.

Gold death-mask, known as 'Mask of Agamemnon.' 16th c. B.C. Shaft Grave V, Mycenae. 26 cm high.

Gold signet ring showing a goddess and ritual dancers, 15th c. B.C. Tomb near Knossos. 2.6 cm wide.

The little white rectangles went on and on, enumerating in the cool and telegraphic style of a museum catalogue all the treasures of the Aegean Gold exhibition. It was only after she had read a dozen or so more that Antonia realized the significance of the two ranks of cards. They were all intended, of course, to accompany and identify the hundred-odd pieces contained in the exhibition when it opened in less than five days. But the row on the right, much the shorter of the two, contained descriptions of objects familiar not only to Antonia and her classical colleagues but to every resident of the city who had looked at television or a newspaper during the last four days.

These were the cards that were to have identified the irreplaceable ancient artifacts that had disappeared from this very room on Thursday night. Antonia read them, too, with a kind of superstitious fervor, as if intense concentration on the details of their dimensions and provenance might somehow bring them back.

Gold double-axes with engraved decoration, c. 1500 B.C., from sacred cave at Arkalochori, Crete. 8 cm wide.

Ceramic jar painted with bulls' heads and double-axes, 16th c. B.C. Pseira, Crete. 77 cm high.

Reconstruction of the Lion Hunt dagger. 37 cm long.

Silver jug with embossed arcade pattern over horizontal fluting, 16th c. B.C. Shaft Grave V, Mycenae. 34.5 cm high.

Gold diadem with embossed Cretan motifs. 16th c. B.C. Shaft Grave III, Mycenae. 65 cm wide.

Gold earrings with granulated conical pendant, 14th–13th c. B.C. Knossos. 3.4 cm high.

Gold scepter with cloisonné enameled globe and two hawks, 12th c. B.C. Cyprus. 16.5 cm high.

Antonia shook herself out of the hypnotic fascination exerted by the little cards and reminded herself that she was supposed to be looking for clues to the whereabouts of Ariadne, not the Aegean Gold. And she adamantly refused to believe that there was any connection between the two.

She turned to Ariadne's desk.

The most striking thing about it was the bareness of its surface. A blotter, two sharpened pencils, copies of the Graduate School catalogue, and the Personnel Directory. No photographs, no postcards or silly gag-gifts from friends, none of the personal clutter that normally encumbers a student's desktop. Still another indication of the barrenness of the girl's personal life, or perhaps only a manifestation of the compulsive neatness Antonia remembered from her term papers and exams.

Systematically, from upper left to lower right, she began to go through the drawers of Ariadne's desk.

Exactly thirty-two minutes after he had left it, Bennie reappeared at the door labeled "Workroom." Antonia was half sitting, half leaning against the edge of Ariadne's desk, a sheaf of papers in one hand. Her head was bent above these papers, causing her long hair to fall like a curtain beside her face, concealing its expression from Bennie. She did not look up when he opened the door, nor when he spoke her name.

"Miss Nielsen?" he said again, a little louder.

This time Antonia raised her head and looked at him, and the expression on her face startled Bennie. She looked dazed and gave no sign that she saw, let alone recognized, him. She glanced around distractedly as if trying to remember where she was.

"You all right, Professor?" Bennie's tone hovered somewhere between impatience and anxiety. "Did you . . . ?"

"Yes," she said vaguely. It was not clear which, if either, of his questions she was answering. She stood up then and turned to Ariadne's desk. Its surface was no longer bare but half covered by three piles of legal-size paper. Antonia laid the set she had been reading on top of one of these piles, consolidated it with the other two, and turned to Bennie with the whole bundle in her arms.

"Must go home now." Again she seemed to be speaking to herself as much as to Bennie. Still clutching the papers, she brushed past him and headed for the door.

In some bewilderment, Bennie glanced around the room, closed a couple of half-open drawers in Ariadne's desk, switched off the lights, and started after her.

He found himself almost trotting to keep up with her long nervous stride, found himself following rather than leading her through the labyrinth of grimy corridors to the side door by which they had entered the museum.

"Look, Miss Nielsen," he began as he unlocked the door, "I'll call you after I . . ."

But Antonia was gone before he finished the sentence. Still moving at the same hectic pace, she waved her free hand in farewell without turning around and soon disappeared in the darkness surrounding the floodlit formal garden.

9

The Clew

AT SEVEN-THIRTY THE NEXT MORNING BENNIE appeared at Antonia's door for the second time in three days. He was nearly as groggy as on the previous occasion, but at least this time he was vertical.

When Antonia opened the door she was fully dressed though barefoot, and Nike only waved her tail in dignified acknowledgment of his arrival. The big Afghan stayed at her post in front of the fireplace, perhaps because there was no obvious way of getting from there to the front door.

Not a trace remained of last night's flurry of housekeeping. The living room looked, in fact, as if it had been more recently bombed than cleaned. Overflowing ashtrays, half-empty coffee cups, a couple of empty highball glasses, and Antonia's discarded sandals competed for every square foot of horizontal surface with a welter of books and papers.

At the epicenter of this mess was a small clear space about eighteen inches square, representing the spot where Antonia had been sitting crosslegged on the floor until the doorbell rang. Nearby were the papers from Ariadne's desk.

Antonia herself looked exhausted but no longer dazed. It was obvious that she was dressed not because she had risen early but because she had never gone to bed. Yet in spite of the shadows under her eyes and the ravaged condition of her hair, there was an air of suppressed excitement about her.

"You found something in that drawer?" Bennie asked.

"*That*, my dear Mr. Thompson, is one of the great understatements of our era." Antonia glanced dubiously around the living room. "You'd better come into the kitchen. There doesn't seem to be anywhere to sit down in here."

The kitchen, though tiny, was in good order and Bennie sank gratefully into one of the two chairs. Nike, having somehow picked her way through the debris in the living room, followed them in and stationed herself suggestively beside a fifty-pound bag of Dog Chow in one corner.

From the sink, where she was rinsing the residue of the night's coffee out of an electric pot, Antonia began, "I had a feeling you'd come here. I seem to remember that I left in rather a hurry last night, and you certainly have a right to an explanation."

"Yeah, I was sorta thinking that myself. But . . ."

"I'm afraid I was in a state of near shock. What I found last night . . ."

"Professor, you're . . ."

"Those papers I found . . ."

Wearily Bennie unwrapped his gangling frame from his chair, stood up, stepped across the narrow space that separated him from Antonia, and grabbed her right wrist. She looked up at him, startled, then followed his gaze down to her hand. It was holding a heaping scoopful of tea that was about to follow its predecessor into the electric coffee-pot. She grinned sheepishly and dumped it back into the canister.

"Look, Mr. Thompson, why don't *you* make the coffee while I go take a cold shower and change my clothes. Your workday may be finished, but mine hasn't started yet, and

I've got to get myself into some semblance of order. We'll talk when I get back." She left him muttering at the unfamiliar coffeepot.

When Antonia reappeared twenty minutes later in a crisp brown pantsuit, with her long caramel hair brushed and shining and tied with an emerald-green ribbon, she looked thoroughly rehabilitated.

"It probably won't last much beyond noon, but for the time being I feel great," she announced. "How's that coffee coming along?"

Bennie looked up glumly from the mug he was nursing between thick dark hands. "Coffee's lousy," he said. "But then the rest of the day ain't shaping up so great neither. Guess what followed me here from the museum, Professor."

Absorbed as she was in the events of the night just past and the morning she somehow still had to get through, Antonia merely looked blank.

"Fuzz, Professor. Cops. The *police*, dig? Think about it real hard, maybe you can figure out what's going through them little tiny minds of theirs. Hell, Professor, they thought they had a burglary on their hands. By now they must be thinking it's a whole goddam conspiracy! Me, Ari, now you—all in it together, that's what they're thinking. Only *I'm* the one that's gonna . . ."

"Hold on, Mr. Thompson. I see what you mean, and I'm sorry I didn't see it before. I'm jeopardizing your job, aren't I? And maybe more than that. I've been so wrapped up in—but it's going to be all right, believe me. When I tell you what—no, let me begin at the beginning."

She poured herself a cup of the lousy coffee, refilled Bennie's mug, and settled herself into the chair opposite his at the small kitchen table.

"Now," she began briskly, "has Ariadne told you what

she and the other graduate students have been doing in the museum? What they were *hired* to do, that is?"

"She ain't said much about it, but it has something to do with sorting out some old documents. Sort of an inventory, like."

"That's the general idea, yes. Except that the 'old documents' are ancient papyri, close to two thousand years old. The museum acquired a sizable batch of them last year. They weren't supposed to be anything very sensational, or we wouldn't have gotten them. But the museum didn't have much papyrus, and we thought they'd be useful as teaching materials in our graduate program, if nothing else.

"Nobody really knew what was in the collection. Presumably it had been screened before it left Egypt, I suppose by some sub-sub-underling in the Archaeological Service. I would hate," she grinned maliciously, "to be in that guy's shoes now. He'll be lucky to get a job selling fake scarabs to tourists at the Great Pyramid."

Bennie looked thoroughly mystified.

"Anyway, the papyri arrived in November. Christmas was coming, the Aegean Gold exhibition was coming, the museum staff couldn't handle any more, and someone got the idea of hiring a few graduate students to do a sort of pre-cataloguing job on them. We were delighted, of course —our kids are always hard up for money, and besides the experience could be very valuable for them professionally. So Roy—Professor Sandler, our chairman—handpicked four of our best doctoral candidates, including Ariadne, gave them a crash course in papyrological scripts, and turned them loose shortly before Christmas.

"And that was the last I heard of the project, not being directly involved in it myself. Except for an occasional secondhand report that the kids were starting to grumble about slave labor and so on. It sounded exciting at first—deciphering real honest-to-goodness ancient papyrus. Maybe they thought they'd stumble across the recipe for *tana*-leaf tea or something."

For the first time Bennie grinned knowingly. "Yeah, like in *The Mummy's Curse*. I saw that three times on TV."

"Well, unfortunately your average papyrus isn't quite that exciting. And anyway these kids weren't supposed to read them or date them or try to fill in missing parts. They aren't equipped to do anything that technical. Their instructions were very explicit. They were simply to puzzle out enough of each document to give a one-line description of its general type—marriage contract, death certificate, bill of receipt, or whatever. That's the sort of thing most of the collection was supposed to be. The idea was that when it was finally turned over to a specialist for serious editing it would be in at least some kind of rough order, rather than just a mass of unidentified documents.

"Their instructions were very explicit on one other point, too. Any papyrus they could not decipher, or which seemed to be in any way out of the ordinary, was to be turned over to a designated member of the museum staff for identification." A more somber note crept into Antonia's voice. "And it is those instructions that our friend Ariadne has disobeyed. Blatantly, rashly, magnificently disobeyed."

"You mean she *stole* one of these—papyruses?" Bennie sounded a little confused. "Aw, come off it, Professor, last week it was pots and necklaces she was 'sposed to of ripped off, and now . . ."

"No, no, Ariadne hasn't stolen anything. Not in the sense you mean, at any rate. But she's *found* something—I still can't believe it myself yet, I keep thinking there must be some mistake. Bennie, she has found one of the lost tragedies of Euripides!"

There was a silence of considerable length while Bennie

gazed at her as if trying to read the answer to some riddle in her face. Finally he said, "I guess—I guess that's pretty good, huh?"

"*Good!*" Antonia was almost shrieking. Now that the words were finally out, now that she was no longer the only person in the world to share Ariadne's astounding secret, the dams of scholarly caution and incredulity burst, and all her pent-up delight and exultation came flooding out. She wondered briefly if the little kitchen table would collapse under her if she leaped up on it and did an impromptu cancan. Deciding it probably would, she contented herself with merely shouting at poor bewildered Bennie.

"*Good!*" she shrieked again. "My dear boy, it's sensational! It's one of the great finds of the century, in a class with the *Dyskolos*, or the Bacchylides papyrus, or—" She stopped abruptly, finally seeing what the expression on Bennie's face meant. He didn't have the foggiest idea what she was talking about.

"I'm sorry," she said more gently, "of course it can't possibly mean as much to a layman. Look, just take my word for it that the manuscript is important in itself. What's important to *us* is what it's going to mean to Ariadne. It's going to be the making of her career, Bennie. It'll mean a really good job, prestige, even fame of a sort. Of course," she added dryly, "the fame is going to look more like notoriety for a while. There'll be a lot of resentment against her, because strictly speaking she had no right to do what she's done."

"What's she done wrong, Professor? She couldn't help finding this papyrus thing, could she? What's wrong with that?"

"Nothing, of course. But having found it and recognized what it is, she was supposed to turn it over to the experts. And she didn't. She had it photographed, transcribed it, edited it, wrote a lengthy introduction—in short, she's very close to having a publishable edition of one of the most dramatic manuscript discoveries of the century."

"And all that gravy shoulda landed on somebody else's plate, right?"

"Right. But the resentment will die down eventually, especially when they see what a solid job she's done. And after that—well, she has an enviable future ahead of her."

"Yeah, I can see that." With meticulous attention to justice, Bennie was apportioning the last of the lousy coffee between their two cups. He was also looking worried.

"All right, Professor," he said, "so Ari's made this great discovery. I dig that. But looks to me like you found something you weren't even looking for. What you *ain't* found is what you *was* looking for. Namely Ari. Far's I can see, we don't know no more'n we did before about where she's got to."

"No, I'm afraid not. But—well, yes, in a way we do know where she is. Or rather where she isn't. Where she *isn't* is in trouble."

"How do you figure that?"

"I think where her career is concerned Ariadne is a very hardheaded, practical person. If her work was going badly, if it was threatened in some way, I can imagine her reacting recklessly. But at a time like this, with the opportunities that will open up to her when this discovery is made public, my guess is that she's being very cautious, very prudent."

"Yeah, maybe." Bennie didn't sound very convinced.

"There'd be idealistic motives as well as practical ones. I strongly suspect that Ariadne sees herself right now—maybe subconsciously—as a sort of divinely appointed guardian to that manuscript. I think she'd take care of herself for *its* sake if for no other reason. Or does that sound too farfetched?"

"No, Ma'am, not for Ari. She *is* kinda weird about

stuff like that, no doubt about it. I just hope trouble ain't
come looking for *her*."

"I don't think it has, Mr. Thompson. But I can tell
you who will be in trouble if she doesn't get her body out
of this chair and on down to the office in the next twenty-
five minutes. In short, I have a nine-thirty class and I've
got to get going. Can I give you a lift somewhere?"

"Thanks, Professor, but I'm going the other way. I can
catch a bus."

As she saw him out the door, Antonia suddenly remembered the obvious.

"Look, Mr. Thompson, I'll explain all this to Lieutenant Caracci this afternoon. My behavior last night was
unorthodox to say the least, and I'll make it clear to him
that the initiative was entirely mine and that you went
along only very reluctantly. I'll have to tell him what I
found, too, and what I think it means. But we mustn't say
anything to anyone else about Ariadne's discovery. We've
stumbled across something she didn't intend anyone to
know about until it was a *fait accompli*—completely finished. I don't know how she'll feel about our knowing about
it, but I'm sure she won't want it to go any further."

"No way I'm gonna talk, Professor." He grinned. "Not
that I could tell anyone much about it even if I wanted to.
It's all Greek to me!"

Antonia sighed ruefully as she closed the door after
him. The line was excruciatingly familiar to classicists, and
it had been about three hundred years since they found it
amusing.

Bennie had not been gone more than ten minutes
when the phone rang. Antonia was stuffing lecture notes
for the nine-thirty class into her briefcase, trying to remember what the subject of the course was. Trying to get the

mental circuits marked "Ariadne" and "Euripides manuscript" to stay in the Off position long enough for her to do
her job.

Still thinking about them, she picked up the phone.

"Professor Nielsen? Steve Caracci. I thought you'd
want to know we picked up the museum burglar last night.
Or one of them. Looks like the character the Thompson
kid told us about. Maybe the one who attacked Professor
Randolph, too."

The mental circuits whirred and buzzed for a moment,
then clicked into place.

"The big man who was talking to Ariadne in the museum that night?"

"Yeah. And it turns out that wasn't so surprising,
either."

"What wasn't?" Antonia hoped she didn't sound as
disoriented as she felt.

"Him being with the girl like that. Because it turns
out this guy we got here is Ariadne Pappas' brother."

❧ 10 ❧

A Pocketful of Gold

TUESDAY, BLESSEDLY, WAS A ONE-CLASS DAY FOR
Antonia, which meant that by eleven o'clock she was free
to sit down and try to assimilate Caracci's announcement.

When he called, just as she was leaving for the class,
she had all but hung up on him. She managed a hasty
"Thanks, Lieutenant, but I'm late for a class. Talk to you
later." Then she resolutely thrust his words to the back of
her mind and refused to think about them until her lecture
was finished.

A ninety-minute lecture is tiring at the best of times.
After a sleepless night, and in combination with shock, excitement, and apprehension, it is apt to leave one considerably less than *compos mentis*. For one rather scary moment Antonia found herself entertaining the possibility
that everything that had happened in the last twelve hours
—her midnight junket to the museum, the Euripides
papyrus, Caracci's call—had been some kind of hallucina-
tion. But the moment passed. She shook her head ferociously to clear it, and went to fetch a cup of black coffee
from the urn in the faculty lounge.

The familiarly execrable brew made everything seem
much more down-to-earth, made it seem no more than
sensible to go downtown and beard Caracci in his own den

for a change. There was some mistake, of course, that was all. The man they had picked up was obviously not Ariadne's brother, for the simple reason that Ariadne didn't have a brother. She had never mentioned a brother. And even if he were somehow related to the strange Pappas clan, that fact wouldn't prove that Ariadne herself had anything to do with the burglary.

The expedition seemed significantly less sensible when Antonia finally stood before the brick and concrete mass of Police Headquarters half an hour later. She thought about having lunch first. She thought about phoning a long-neglected friend in Topeka. She thought she'd better go on in before she lost her nerve.

But Caracci, after she had threaded a maze of institution-colored corridors to his office, didn't seem particularly surprised to see her. He even reached a welcoming handshake to her over a desk of battleship-gray steel.

"Afternoon, Professor." He glanced at his watch to check the accuracy of this greeting. "Glad you came. There's a couple things I . . ."

"Look, Lieutenant," Antonia interrupted, "what's this nonsense about Ariadne's brother? She doesn't *have* a brother."

"Yes, Ma'am, so we were led to believe too. But the sister has confirmed it. He's their brother all right. But I got the idea they don't exactly advertise his existence."

"But where . . . how did you . . . ?"

"We went back to the Pappas place yesterday to have another try at questioning the mother and sister. And there he was at the kitchen table eating dinner with 'em, big as life. Or slightly bigger."

"But what makes you so sure he's the thief?"

"He tried to bolt when he saw us, out a window. Since the window happened to be on the second floor, I thought it might be a good idea to try and stop him. Fought like a wild bull, though."

"But that still doesn't . . ."

Caracci's voice went on, patient and implacable, ignoring the interruption. "In his pockets we found a few odds and ends. A couple of earrings that don't match, and a ring, and a thing that looked like a miniature battle-ax about two inches long. Might have been a child's toy, except it was made of solid gold. All the stuff was solid gold, Miss Nielsen."

Antonia had ignored the chair he offered her when she entered, but she sat down now, heavily, feeling suddenly overwhelmed with weariness.

"It isn't a toy, Lieutenant," she said dully. "It's a votive *labrys*, an offering to a war deity. Maybe Pallas Athene herself. They've found a lot of them in Crete. It's also a symbol of the House of Minos, the House of the Double Axe. The Labyrinth."

"Yes, Ma'am." Antonia scarcely heard the note of sympathy in his voice. "That's what Miss Lilly said too. We had her in here this morning to identify the things. Now, Miss Nielsen, I'm sorry but I have to ask you about last . . ."

"Lieutenant, you said on the phone that you'd caught *one* of the museum burglars. Just what was that supposed to mean?"

"Professor Nielsen, try to look at this from our point of view." Caracci sounded a little weary himself now. "This man's sister—*and* her friend Bennie Thompson—are both museum employees. The girl certainly, and Thompson very possibly, are under financial pressure. Miss Pappas has been missing for almost five days. And now there's one new factor, too. This Pappas kid—he's only about eighteen—had stuff from the museum in his pocket all right. What he doesn't have, in my opinion, is the brains to plan or carry out a burglary. My best guess at the moment is that he talked, or forced, his sister into cooperating with him, with or without Thompson's help."

"I suppose he could have held a gun on her, if that's what you mean. But I'm more certain than ever that Ariadne isn't responsible—morally or legally—for the museum theft. I think you were about to ask me what I was doing at the museum last night."

"Yes, Ma'am, I was."

"I was searching Ariadne's desk. I knew you'd probably been through it, but I suddenly got the idea that you people might have missed something, something that only a classicist would be able to recognize as important."

"Really, Miss Nielsen, that's . . ."

"I know, I know, highly irregular. But I did find something—or rather Ariadne did. She's made a once-in-a-lifetime discovery, Lieutenant, a rare and very ancient manuscript that's going to be the making of her career. She'd have to be very stupid, or very impatient, to jeopardize all that—and Ariadne is neither stupid nor impatient. She's worked hard for years, she's had an astounding stroke of luck, the rewards are just around the corner. She'd have to be crazy to get involved in a crime at a time like this, even if she were capable of it under ordinary circumstances."

"All right then, let's say she was forced to cooperate. I still want to find her and talk to her."

With what she regarded as saintly forbearance, Antonia refrained from pointing out that this was precisely what she herself had been trying to do for the better part of a week now. Instead she shifted to a new tack.

"What about her so-called brother? I suppose he denies that Ariadne's involved?"

Caracci shrugged wearily. "I really couldn't tell you what he denies or what he admits, Miss Nielsen. He hasn't spoken six words since we brought him in last night."

"Could I talk to him?"

"No, Ma'am, I'm afraid you couldn't. He's with our tame psychiatrist right now. And I doubt you'd get anything out of him anyway. I doubt even the shrink will get him to talk, and he's pretty good at it, as a rule. But this one, I dunno, I don't see him talking for anyone. If I hadn't heard him say his name last night for the sergeant, I'd be wondering if he *could* talk. What he reminds me of is some kind of wild animal with its foot in a trap, just sitting and waiting, real patient and quiet—and dangerous."

"Very poetic, Lieutenant. Do you always wax so lyrical over your prisoners?"

"No, Ma'am," said Caracci, unbaitable as ever. "This one's different. This one is *real* different."

The neighborhood was quiet and shady, with many old trees and carefully tended shrubs and flowerbeds, a miniature suburbia set down in the heart of the city five blocks from campus. It was also a faculty enclave, and its elderly but comfortable houses were the envy of the younger professors who dreamed of walking to work every morning but who had to settle for a high-rise apartment at the other end of a forty-five-minute bus ride.

The Randolphs' house was distinguishable from its fellows mainly by the neatness of its front sidewalk, which was unencumbered by the strollers, skateboards, and bicycles cluttering the approaches to the other homes on the street. It was not unique in its need of a fresh paint job, but contrived to make its lack of sparkle look like a mark of character rather than shabbiness.

Antonia was thinking of the Randolphs rather than their house as she approached it. She was fairly certain of finding them both at home, but it was anyone's guess what Gillian's mood might be. She had undoubtedly sensed by now that Win was staying home from the office today in order to babysit with his unstable wife, and she was probably resenting it. But if Ariadne was in some kind of serious trouble, Gillian's precious moods would just have to take a back seat for the time being. Antonia squared her shoulders and marched almost defiantly up the Randolphs' sidewalk.

It was Win who answered the doorbell. There was a note of relief in his voice as he said, "Oh, it's you, Antonia," as if he had feared it might be someone—or something—much worse. Even so he made no move to open the screen door and let her in, but stood awkwardly behind it peering out at her. Ignoring his obvious reluctance to talk to her, Antonia pulled the screen door open herself and plunged *in medias res.*

"Win, I'm sorry to barge in like this, but things are starting to look really serious for Ariadne. We've got to find her!"

"All right, all right," Win said, "come on in. But really, Antonia, I've already told you—" He stepped aside to let her pass, then shut the front door behind her.

The living room curtains were closed against the afternoon sun, and it took Antonia's eyes a minute to adjust to the half-light they allowed to filter through. When she could see Win's face clearly at last, it looked haggard and preoccupied. The disappearance of Ariadne Pappas was quite obviously the last thing he had, or wanted to have, on his mind. He seemed in fact to be listening for something, and a few minutes later Antonia caught him glancing up the stairs that led from the living room to the second-floor bedrooms. So it *was* Gillian, she thought. Probably she'd caught them in the middle of a row of some sort. Well, it couldn't be helped.

"Now what's all this about Ariadne?" Win tried for his tut-tut-my-girl-everything's-going-to-be-all-right tone, but it didn't come off very well.

"Her brother's in jail. He was picked up last night with some trinkets from the Aegean Gold exhibition still in his pocket. So of course the police are more convinced than ever that Ariadne is somehow mixed up in the museum burglary. The most charitable interpretation they're prepared to put on the situation is that she may have been forced to . . ."

"Now hold on, Antonia. You've lost me already. You're saying the museum burglar is Ariadne's *brother*?" For the first time he looked as if he was actually listening to her, and listening very intently at that.

"*One* of the burglars, is the way they put it."

"And so the fuzz instantly deduce that Ariadne . . ." He paused for a moment as if contemplating the unsoundable depths of the law's stupidity.

"Exactly. And it's the worst possible time for it, from Ariadne's point of view."

"There's a *good* time to fall under suspicion of theft?"

"No, of course not. But now of all times— Look, Win, has Ariadne said anything to you about a, well, about a discovery she's made?"

The expression on Win's face was memorable but not easy to decipher. In swift succession surprise, annoyance, fear, defensiveness, and resignation flicked across his features like the picture cards that a child riffles with his thumb to produce a primitive movie. But his voice was calm when he spoke.

"I guess she must have changed her mind," he said thoughtfully. "I understood no one else was to know. But yes—to answer your question—she did consult me about it once."

"She didn't change her mind. I came across the manuscript—or rather Ariadne's photographs of it—more or less by accident. I didn't intend to mention it to anyone, but under the circumstances . . ."

"Yes, I see what you mean." Win still looked as if he was thinking hard. "Nice batch of headlines it would make. 'Coed Steals Priceless Ancient Manuscript Plus King's Ransom in Gold.' "

"She hasn't *stolen* the papyrus," Antonia protested.

"No, of course not. But a lot of noses in the profession are going to be sadly out of joint nonetheless. And if she's simultaneously making headlines in connection with the burglary—whew!"

"So what do we do? There must be *some* way of locating her. Could she have gone out of town to do research in another library? Or to talk to a publisher maybe? Or how about a laboratory, to get the papyrus dated? Where's the nearest carbon-14 lab, anyway?"

"I couldn't say, Antonia" His momentary surge of enthusiasm for the Perils of Ariadne seemed to have passed, and once again he sounded bored with the subject. "All of the aforementioned are possibilities, I suppose, but she's said nothing to me about going anywhere to do anything. Really, Antonia, you've got to relax and let our lovable local gumshoes handle this mess. Charmingly inept though they are, they do seem to be making some progress on the burglary, and as for Ariadne . . ." He paused, looking a bit grim. "Ariadne's a lot tougher than she looks, believe me. A *lot* tougher. Ariadne can take care of . . ."

He was interrupted by a faint sound as of someone choking on a drink swallowed too hastily. It came from the direction of the stairs leading up to the second floor, and Antonia was afraid she knew what it meant. As she and Win turned in unison toward the stairway, her suspicion was confirmed.

Gillian stood stiffly on the fourth or fifth step up from the level of the living room, looking down at them and torturing a damp handkerchief with her long fingers. She looked as if she had been crying, but now she was trying to make a smile stay in place on her lips, without much success.

After a moment, she abandoned the pretense of a social smile, and the expression that remained on her face was an unlovely compound of laughter, contempt, and horror. Before Win and Antonia could think of anything to say or do, she spoke. Her voice was hoarse and unsteady, but the words were clear enough.

"Can she, Win? Can she take care of herself? I shouldn't like to bet on it, myself. Then again, she may *take care* of the lot of us. The whole bloody, bloody . . ." Her voice broke and she turned and stumbled up the stairs.

11

Fedra

ANTONIA STOOD AT HER APARTMENT-SIZE ELECTRIC range, staring unseeingly at the hamburger. It had been frying now for twelve and a half minutes, and she had long since forgotten all about it. Nike sat nearby drinking in like some Homeric deity the ambrosial fragrance of the smoking meat. It was beginning to look as if she might get more than the fragrance for dinner, as the charring of the hamburger progressed apace. Nike blessed, not for the first time, the unaccountable fastidiousness of humans in matters of meat.

Antonia had cleared away the cups and saucers and coffeepot she and Bennie Thompson had used eight hours earlier. She was thinking now of the other mess, as yet unreclaimed, that still occupied her living room. On the one hand, she felt guilty about Ariadne's typescript, scattered chaotically over furniture and floor, to say nothing of her own books spread-eagled on the arms of chairs and the corners of tables—hardly appropriate treatment for one of the most exciting manuscript discoveries of the century.

On the other hand—she gazed idly at the smoke that rose in ever-increasing volume from the hamburger—there was a streak of sentimentality in Antonia that resolutely opposed the idea of cleaning up the living room. That

clutter of books, papers, and photostats was the visible
reminder of a once-in-a-lifetime experience, a night spent
alone in the company of a manuscript that only a handful
of people had seen for nearly two thousand years. The
peculiar mixture of excitement, incredulity, and awe she
had felt during the six or seven hours between the time
she fled from the museum with Ariadne's papers under her
arm and the moment when she opened her door to Bennie
—no, that would never come again. And to clear away the
clutter that night had left behind would be to distance the
memory of it, not to lose it but to put it behind her, to file
it away in the past. She wanted to savor it a little longer
before she did that.

Since Bennie's appearance on her doorstep at seven-
thirty that morning, she had hardly had time to draw a
deep breath, let alone to ponder the implications of
Ariadne's wonderful discovery. There had been the explanation to Bennie, the morning class, the confrontations
with Caracci and the Randolphs, the continuing anxiety
about Ariadne herself—not a moment to brood in solitary
glee over the tattered sheets of papyrus that would mean
so much to their discoverer and to every classicist in the
world.

Suddenly she sprang back from the stove, one hand
clapped to her right cheek, which had been stung by
a spatter from the martyred hamburger. Belatedly she
glanced down at her ruined dinner. It was clearly beyond
salvaging, and she dumped it into Nike's bowl without
regret. Then she took a can of beer from the fridge and
carried it into the living room. One armchair had somehow
escaped the general inundation there, and Antonia flopped
wearily into it to sip and dream.

Ariadne's lengthy introduction to her edition of the
papyrus had revealed a streak of romanticism in her that
Antonia had not suspected. With surprising warmth of

imagination, the girl had traced the manuscript's long history from the heyday of the Roman Empire to the late twentieth century.

Its story began in the second century, around the time of the philosopher–emperor Marcus Aurelius. Somewhere in Upper Egypt a nameless family of Greeks or Hellenized Egyptians had bought a scroll containing some of the tragedies of Euripides. They were not rich people, and the roll on which the plays were transcribed was a modest one —second-grade papyrus, narrow margins, handwriting no more than passable. The purchasers, or their descendants, had not greatly prized their Euripides: in the following century they cut the roll into separate sheets and wrote their household accounts on the blank sides.

By the time this supply of makeshift scratch paper was exhausted, the accounts told a grim tale of the family's decline and fall. Bit by bit cattle, furniture, and slaves were sold off to pay the Emperor's tax collectors, and year by year the taxes grew heavier. Finally—impossible to guess when, even to the century—the house was abandoned, to sink slowly to ruin above the old account sheets and other odds and ends of papyrus. Very likely the last occupants had taken to the roads like thousands of their countrymen, to become vagabonds and worse on the highways of the dying province.

Such was the manuscript's ancient history as Ariadne had pieced it together. It was a plausible account, though not demonstrably true in every detail; ancient history seldom is. But this particular papyrus had an even more tenuous pedigree than most. It had not been unearthed by a legitimate archaeological expedition but had "come into the hands" of the Egyptian government, from which the university had acquired it. This noncommittal phrase very likely meant that the papyri had been discovered by site-robbers who for once had been caught red-handed by the Archaeological Service. In any case, the place and circumstances of the find were unknown and unknowable, except that the Egyptians had passed on to the American purchasers their source's statement that the papyri had all been found together "under a staircase in a ruined house."

Antonia sighed and shook her beer can to see whether it was as empty as it felt. It was. Deciding she was too tired to return to the smoky kitchen for another, she settled deeper into the armchair, closed her eyes, and sank back into her reverie.

Her thoughts turned from the physical survival of the papyrus to the play itself.

It had been known for generations that Euripides wrote such a tragedy. Like many ancient authors, the youngest of Athens' great tragedians left a legacy of titles —works lost but known to have existed—that far outnumbered his surviving works. Often these titles come down to us clad in a few skimpy rags of text—three words quoted by a scholiast, half a dozen mutilated verses from a scrap of papyrus the size of a playing card. These fragments are painstakingly collected, arranged, emended, annotated, and analyzed, published between austere covers of gold-stamped maroon or dark blue, and roundly applauded as the choicest fruits of philological *wissenschaft*. Yet the fact remains that such works, however draped in meticulously edited *fragmenta*, are still for all practical purposes well and truly "lost."

So it was with a strange play of Euripides' middle years called *The Cretans*. It consisted, until Ariadne's papyrus appeared, of twenty verses quoted by Porphyry, fifty more (very fragmentary) preserved on one of the Oxyrhynchus papyri, and another fifty in good condition on a parchment in Berlin.

And that was all that remained of Euripides' version of the horrendous tale of the House of Minos. Sacrilege, perversion, and vengeance—the old legend had offered Euripides a plot as sensational as anything in the "liberated" twentieth-century repertoire. How had he treated it? Three generations of scholars had argued the point, with dubious results. Some said Euripides held the guilty queen responsible for her act, despite the brilliance of the self-defense he wrote for her (preserved in the Berlin fragment). It would not, they argued, be the first time a Sophist-trained playwright had played devil's advocate with such devastating plausibility that the audience was hard put to know whose side he was on.

But other scholars held that the queen's words were intended as valid self-justification, that she was indeed what she claimed to be—scapegoat for an impious and despotic king, a man who had tried to cheat a god more ingeniously cruel than himself, her husband.

Well, they would soon know, Antonia told herself groggily. They would soon know what antiquity's most iconoclastic playwright had made of Queen Pasiphaë. They would soon. . . .

If the phone had rung three minutes later than it did, it probably would have been powerless to wake Antonia. As it was, she heaved herself out of the armchair, staggered blindly down the abbreviated hallway to the kitchen, stumbled over Nike, who had posted herself in the doorway, and scooped up the receiver on the sixth or seventh ring.

The girl's voice was uncharacteristically diffident, almost frightened.

"Miss Nielsen? This is Fedra Pappas. Ariadne's sister?"

In its dazed condition, Antonia's mind produced a surrealistic montage of the following impressions:

Next she'll be telling me she's calling from the palace at Knossos.

It's odd I didn't realize it before, but I'd never been told her name.

Her brother—she's just heard about her brother.

The Princess of Crete, who became Queen of Athens by marrying the man her sister had loved.

It wasn't just a hobby with their father, then, it was an obsession.

As her brain slowly cleared, the girl was saying, ". . . if I could meet you somewhere."

"I'll be glad to see you tomorrow afternoon, Miss Pappas. I have classes in the . . ."

Five minutes later, shuddering under a cold shower, Antonia was trying to remember the Aristophanic polysyllable that meant "unintelligent person (f.) who allows herself to be persuaded too easily; gullible idiot." She couldn't remember the word, but it was obvious that Aristophanes had her in mind when he coined it. She cursed Aristophanes, herself, Fedra Pappas, and, for good measure, the Greek third declension as she climbed into a taxi and headed downtown.

The aspiring English pub was no darker on Tuesday evening than it had been on Sunday afternoon, but at least now the murk seemed less artificial. Two persons of unidentifiable age and sex were actually throwing darts through it, in the general direction of the dartboard. The Pappas girl, as far as Antonia could tell, had not yet arrived. She chose the booth nearest the door and started to sit down on the bench that faced the entrance. Then she thought, to hell with that, let *her* look for *me*, and seated herself defiantly with her back to the door.

Her peevish mood, born of exhaustion, lasted only until Fedra appeared five minutes later. She looked tired, too—tired and scared—and Antonia's resentment soon softened.

It was not the shock of her brother's arrest that had upset the girl, Antonia quickly discovered.

"Oh, he'll be all right," she said. "The worst they can do is put him in some kind of home or something. And maybe that wouldn't be such a bad idea either. For him *or* us. I'm afraid it was Yanni that jumped Professor Randolph last Saturday, though I don't know why. Probably something just panicked him and he attacked the first thing he saw moving. I'm glad Professor Randolph wasn't hurt, but the next person he picks on might not be so lucky. Several nights last week, including Saturday, Yanni was gone for several hours. We don't know where he went, but I bet he was hanging around the museum hoping to see Ari. Usually she comes home to see him pretty regular, once a week or so, but these last few months she couldn't because of working so hard on that thesis or whatever you call it. So she taught Yanni how to take the bus from our neighborhood to the museum and back, so he could visit her whenever he wanted and not feel like he was abandoned. Made him feel real proud too, moving around the city by himself like that. At first he went back and forth a lot, like he was just showing off that he knew how."

"But I don't understand why you . . ."

"Look, I went down there this morning and saw him. Mamá wasn't about to go, and there wasn't anyone else to do it. He wouldn't talk to me, I didn't really expect he would, but I know that look he had. I never saw it but once before, but I never forgot it either." She paused, frowned, took a pull at the mug of ale Antonia had ordered for her.

"Maybe it was because I was just a kid myself at the time. It must have been about ten years ago, while Ari was still in high school. Well, one day she got appendicitis and they rushed her to the hospital to get operated on. Seeing it was her, naturally they made a big fuss about it. If it'd been me, I probably would've had to walk myself to the hospital.

"So anyway I was left at home to take care of Yanni. I didn't pay much attention to him, but after a while I began to notice something was wrong. He never talked much anyway, but that day I couldn't get him to say anything. He just sat and stared and brooded till I thought I'd go crazy. I finally got so mad I threw something at him. Not to hurt him, you know, just some little thing to bring him out of that trance he was in. Well, I hit him all right, right on the cheek, and he never even blinked. After that I left him alone. I think it sort of scared me, him sitting there like a statue, not moving or making a sound no matter what I did to him. Like I said, I was only a kid—I must've been about ten at the time—and I couldn't understand what was wrong with him. But I know now, and that's what's worrying me."

"I'm afraid I don't quite follow that."

"It was Ari. Nobody bothered to explain to him why they were taking her away so suddenly, or when she'd be back. Probably Ari wasn't in any condition to talk to him herself, and it never would've occurred to the rest of us. So he just sat there like that for six days, until they brought her back. When she finally did come home, he acted funny too. At first it was like he was scared of her—wouldn't look at her or talk to her or stay alone in the same room with her. Afterwards, when he got used to her being back again, it was just the opposite—he wouldn't let her out of his sight."

"That's very touching, Miss Pappas, but I still don't see what it has to do . . ."

"The point is, Professor, I finally found out what it was that was bugging him. Somehow he'd gotten it into his head that Ari was never coming back. As a matter of fact—he thought she was dead." Fedra bit the end of the sentence off savagely, as if it had a bad taste that she wanted to get out of her mouth as quickly as possible. For good measure she also took another gulp of the ale. They were both silent for a long minute.

"But surely you're not suggesting that your brother is thinking that *now*."

"Yes, Ma'am, that's exactly what I *am* suggesting. Of course, he's probably got it all wrong, just like he did that other time, but I think he *thinks* she's gone away forever or died or something. I think he *thinks* he'll never see her again."

"Look, Miss Pappas, before we start speculating about what may or may not have become of Ariadne, and what your brother may or may not think has become of her, I'd like to know more about their relationship. I've gotten some rather conflicting impressions about that." She was remembering Caracci's words: *My guess is, he forced her to cooperate. . . .*

Again the calculating look passed over Fedra's face as it had Sunday afternoon. But this time her mental arithmetic seemed to go more quickly.

"All right," she said, "I don't see what good it'll do, but then I don't see anything else that's going to help either. You're the brainy one at this table. Maybe if you had more to go on you could figure something." She fortified herself with another swig of ale, tossed her black hair, and plunged ahead.

"Yanni, see, he's our half-brother really. It's not a

pretty story and I don't know all the details, but apparently Mamá went on the warpath one time when I was about two. She and my father weren't exactly an ideal model couple, and she was always getting mad about something or other. Anyway, this one night she walked out, and when she came back a few days later she was pregnant. Naturally she didn't want the kid, and personally I got an idea she tried to get rid of him, maybe even messed him up some seeing how he turned out. Anyway, Yanni got born in spite of her, and when Babás saw him . . ." The long black eyebrows lifted eloquently.

"You mean your father knew from the beginning that the child wasn't his?"

Fedra snorted. "He'd have had to be a lot dumber than he was not to see *that*, Miss Nielsen. Whatever problems my father might have had, black blood wasn't one of 'em. And this kid was black.

"Now what you have to remember is, Babás didn't really live in twentieth-century America like you and me. At heart he was just an old-fashioned Greek farmer, a small olive grower from one of the most out-of-it parts of Greece. Practically a medieval peasant. So you can imagine what he musta been thinking every time he looked at his wife's black baby. I mean, it was bad enough she was cheating, and it was worse she got knocked up—but a *black baby*! I think that was what he died of, even if it took him nine years to do it. Not that he ever said much. Maybe if he had it wouldn't have eaten at him like it did. Only once or twice that I can remember did he drink a little too much *ouzo* and start in on Mamá. Just words, of course, he'd never have laid a finger on her, but he sure knew a lot of words. He'd start with the one for whore and never stop till he hit omega. Didn't hardly ever repeat himself either. Greek's a hell of a language for cussing, you got to give it that." She grinned appreciatively at the memory of her father's eloquence, finished her ale, and signaled to the waiter for another.

"There was one name he used to call her," Fedra went on, "that I never could figure out. Maybe you'd know what it meant. Passy-something."

Antonia saw that there was no hope of ignoring the implied question. The girl was looking straight at her, waiting for an answer.

"Pasiphaë, probably. She was a queen. A queen of Crete who was unfaithful to her husband."

"Yeah, that was it." Mercifully, she seemed satisfied with this bowdlerized version of the legend of Pasiphaë. But Antonia might have saved herself the trouble of trying to spare the girl's feelings. Ignorant though she was of Greek mythology, Fedra had long since recognized instinctively the depth of her father's bitterness against her mother, as her next words showed.

"Anyway, like I said, it was Yanni's blackness that messed up my father's mind more than anything else. I used to wonder if he wouldn't have been less hurt and less angry if it'd been an animal Mamá was with."

"And yet he raised the child."

"Not really. Oh, he let him live in the house all right, but it was Ari who raised him. Just about the earliest thing I can remember is her taking care of both of us. She must've been about nine, and already Yanni was nearly as big as she was, but she fed him and played with him and kept him quiet so he wouldn't call attention to himself. Attention generally meant trouble where Yanni was concerned. Things were pretty peaceful as long as our parents weren't reminded he was there. As long as they didn't have to actually *look* at him. When they did—you remember the sign? You saw it the other day when you came to the *taverna*."

Through the gathering mists of exhaustion and strong ale, Antonia conjured up an image of the crude bull's head on the childish body. The vague distaste she had felt for the painting turned slowly to horror as she realized what Fedra was driving at.

"You mean that—thing—was supposed to be your *brother*? And it was your father who painted it?"

"Yes, Ma'am, that's what I mean. When he *had* to look at him, that's what Babás saw, I guess. Like he was half animal. I told you it was sort of a joke. Like calling me Fedra. That's not my real name, you know. But Babás had this crazy idea we were like a family in some old legend. The mother was that Passy-what's-her-name, and Ariadne was her daughter, and there was this bull-monster mixed up in it someway. My father said there was a younger daughter too, but she didn't have anything to do with the story. And I pestered him to tell me her name too, because I hated being left out all the time. Finally he told me it was Fedra, and that's what he always called me after that."

"I can't say I care for your father's sense of humor."

"Yeah, me neither. But it didn't used to bother me much when I was a kid. Like I said, that sign made a good target. You know how kids are to each other. Insensitive, like. Ari was the only one that ever saw things from Yanni's point of view. All the rest of us—me, our parents, the kids in the neighborhood, even the teachers—all we saw was this huge, ugly kid that looked dangerous and acted stupid. Ari somehow knew he was just a little kid, and hurt and lonely and scared because everybody hated him and he couldn't figure out why. That all seems pretty obvious now, I guess. But it didn't look so obvious when I was only eleven or twelve. What was obvious *then* was, if I didn't join the other kids in teasing Yanni, they were gonna think I was as creepy as he was. And I didn't have that kind of guts, and Ari did.

"Anyway, now he's in trouble and she's not around to help him, and there's no one else he trusts. Certainly not me or Mamá. I know what Ari'd do if she was here. She'd march right into his cell with one of their old books and . . ."

"Books? Now wait a minute—surely your brother isn't the intellectual type? I had the impression . . ."

"Yes, Ma'am, it's true Yanni isn't what you'd call real bright. But this is different. I was talking about *their* books, the ones Ari used to show him when he was little to keep him quiet. I don't know how much he understood of the words, but they had lots of pictures and I always thought it was mostly the attention he liked anyway. It was almost like he was hypnotized or something. He'd just sit there looking sort of dreamy, staring at those old pillars and things, and listening to her voice."

"Pillars. You mean these books were about Greek art or archaeology—temples and so forth?"

"Yes, Ma'am. And legends too, I think. He liked the parts about Crete, because Ari told him that's where our ancestors came from. I remember some of the pictures— gold cups, and those funny-looking axes they had, and all sorts of things with pictures of bulls on 'em. He loved that stuff—it'd always calm him down faster than anything else when he was upset. That's what Ari would do now, I figure —talk to him till he was calm and dreamy and ready to tell the cops what really happened to that museum stuff."

"Unfortunately, they already know what happened to some of it."

Once more Fedra gave a derisive snort. "Yeah, sure. But for my money that stuff they found on him just proves the opposite of what they want it to."

"What do you mean?"

"Come on, Professor, did you ever hear of a thief so stupid he lets the fuzz find him, eating supper in his own house four days after a burglary, with the stuff in his *pockets*? All *that* proves is, he isn't bright enough to rob a museum. Which he isn't."

The fog in Antonia's brain was closing in fast now, and the logic of Fedra's argument seemed irrefutable. The corollary occurred to her with preternatural swiftness.

"Then," she observed brilliantly, "all we have to do is find out how those things *did* get into your brother's pocket!"

There was an embarrassed silence while they both tried to decide how to deal with the fatuity of this remark. Antonia finally concluded that honesty would be, if not the best, at any rate the most dignified policy.

"Miss Pappas," she said, "I'm sorry, but obviously I'm no earthly use to anyone right now. I've had no sleep since night before last, I've drunk two and a half mugs of ale I didn't need, and I have classes to teach tomorrow morning. So let me go home now and sleep on all this, and I'll call you tomorrow noon." She rose to go, but before she started for the door—slowly, with immense dignity and no staggering—Antonia said, "I think you may be right about your brother. That he's hiding something, I mean. And not the museum burglary, either."

12

A Rope of Paper

ARIADNE WAS DANCING. HER LONG BLACK HAIR, NO longer pulled severely back into a ponytail, swung heavy and shining about her bare shoulders and down her back. Something that looked like a golden tiara gleamed dimly on her forehead, just above the long straight eyebrows. The smile playing about her lips combined triumph with a hint of mockery, but her great dark eyes were unreadable.

Behind her, appearing, disappearing, reappearing from what looked like heavy banks of yellow fog or mist, was a motley little band of men and women. Motley, Antonia decided, was the only word for a group that included Caracci in the dark blue uniform and peaked cap of an ordinary patrolman, Win Randolph in his inevitable tweed jacket and slacks and with Gillian at his side, Bennie in faded jeans and a sweatshirt with "Property of the University Museum" printed on the back. Oddest of all was the old man with disheveled gray hair and beard carrying a large roll of papyrus under his arm, his ankle-length chiton draped over one shoulder leaving half his chest exposed. Behind him, at the very end of this ill-assorted procession, came a tall caftan-clad figure with caramel-colored hair piled high on her head and a fistful of glossy travel brochures in one hand. (That, thought Antonia with objectivity, is supposed to be me.)

It was hard at first to make out what these people were doing, but gradually she realized that they were performing a kind of primitive dance, a chain dance or serpentine with Ariadne at its head. It wound its way monotonously in and out of the yellow mist that turned out to be a maze of forsythia hedges in full bloom.

It seemed altogether natural and unremarkable to Antonia that the dancers were linked together, not by joined hands but by a long tannish ribbon of what she somehow knew were strips of papyrus glued together. (That, observed Antonia severely, is *not* what Theophrastus means when he says that papyrus was used for making rope, as well as paper and a lot of other useful things.)

Ariadne held the end of this unlikely strand loosely, even heedlessly, in her left hand, seeming not to take very seriously her role as leader or guide, if that *was* her role. She seemed more intent on something she was hearing or trying to hear. Perhaps the *aulos*, which was the dance's only accompaniment. Or a bell tree?

A telephone. Definitely a telephone. Someone ought to answer it. Antonia ought to answer it. Antonia answered it, fighting one arm free of the twisted bedsheets in order to reach it.

"Hu'o?" she grunted into the receiver.

"Professor Nielsen?" The voice was brisk, alert, cleanly articulated. It had obviously been awake for hours. "Steve Caracci again. Look, I don't intend to make a habit of phoning you every morning, but I'm afraid I have a favor to ask." If he was expecting her to make encouraging noises before he continued, he was disappointed. The sound that came over the wire was more in the nature of a muffled groan.

"Yes, well, as I told you yesterday, our psychiatrist has examined the Pappas boy. He got practically nothing out of him, which is unusual. But he thinks the kid is probably slightly retarded, and he did find out one other thing that's kind of interesting. The boy is extremely sensitive to any mention of his sister—the older one, that is, Ariadne. It seems he . . ."

"Yes, I think I know something about that, Lieutenant. But what do I have to do with all this?"

"Just this, Miss Nielsen. The shrink thinks there may be a chance, just a chance, that the boy would open up to someone—a woman, preferably—that he could identify with his sister, someone who knows her and cares about her. The mother or the other sister would be the obvious choice, of course. But Mrs. Pappas flatly refuses to co-operate, and when the girl tried . . ."

"Yes, I know." *He wouldn't talk to me, I didn't really expect he would.* "And you think it would be public spirited if I were to come down and stick *my* head in the lion's mouth, right?"

"Yes, Ma'am, that's about it. It's a long shot, like I said, but . . ."

"All right, Lieutenant. But it'll have to be after lunch. I have classes to teach this morning."

"Of course, of course. At your convenience, Miss Nielsen. We'll be expecting you sometime this afternoon, then. And thanks."

After this unpromising debut, the morning turned out surprisingly well. Antonia always liked Wednesdays anyway. By Wednesday one has settled back into harness, the stress of reentry into the working week has passed, and Friday still seems too remote to be tantalizing. Moreover, on this particular Wednesday the weather continued spring-like, she had had a good night's sleep and a hearty break-fast, and one of her students asked an intelligent question in class.

It was therefore in a more buoyant mood than she had enjoyed for several days that Antonia collected her coffee and returned to her office after her second class. She tried to concentrate on a long-neglected batch of quiz papers, but her thoughts kept returning to the tangle of incidents and personalities that surrounded Ariadne.

At the moment, she was inclined to view the situation in a relatively optimistic light. Ariadne herself, Antonia was increasingly certain, had simply gone on a trip related to her great discovery. Her study of the papyrus contained, for example, no reference to radiocarbon confirmation of the date she had assigned to it on paleographical grounds. Sooner or later this confirmation would have to be obtained, and it was easy to imagine the excited girl rushing off to the nearest carbon-14 lab, five-millimeter scraps of papyrus in a plastic envelope in her purse, prepared to bully and badger and wheedle the technicians into doing a rush job on her precious manuscript. Ordinarily it would take months to get a dating out of the overworked labs, and this surely was one time Ariadne would have no patience with orthodox procedures. It would be interesting to know what account she had given the lab people of herself and her papyrus. The least devious of women under normal circumstances, Ariadne was undoubtedly capable of prodigies of invention in such a cause as this. Antonia grinned to herself, wishing she had been there to witness the scene. Wherever "there" might be.

She also wished Ariadne would come back from "there" and straighten out her brother. His disorientation, not to mention the golden artifacts found in his pockets, was disturbing, though even the police had to admit that poor Yanni wasn't likely to have planned and carried out the museum burglary unaided. But who had used him, then, or coerced him into collaborating? Certainly not Ariadne, but what about her sister, Fedra, whose sense of exclusion and deprivation was so strong, and whose determination to "get out" was so ruthless?

But if not Yanni and some unknown confederate, then who *had* stolen the Aegean Gold? The question seemed as far from being answered as ever. Unless, of course, one entertained the possibility that Bennie Thompson . . . She thrust the thought aside. Still, it was true he had seemed jumpy and irritable Monday night when she went prowling in the museum. Could there be something there he was afraid she might find out? Hadn't he said something about not having any secrets left after she and the police got through snooping around? But on the other hand, he hadn't made any move to prevent her leaving the museum, hadn't in any way threatened her the next morning when he came to the apartment. If there was anything that Bennie was anxious to conceal, she evidently hadn't found it.

Twenty minutes into the quizzes, Antonia was interrupted by the arrival of Doris, the Classics secretary. She was looking puzzled and a little anxious.

"Mr. Sandler asked me to ask you if you could stop at the Randolphs' on your way home to lunch and . . . ah . . ." She stopped in confusion.

"And what?"

"Well, the fact is, Professor Randolph never came to work this morning. He had two classes, at nine and ten, and he didn't show up for either of them. His students have been . . ."

"But couldn't you phone him?"

"Oh yes, I tried that, of course. Several times, in fact. But there was no answer."

"All right, Doris, I'll look in on my way home." Antonia's voice was casual, almost cool. She did not think Doris was deceived, though. They both knew that, while it is not unheard of for a teacher to turn up for a class half

prepared, half asleep, or half sloshed, it is extremely unlikely that he will fail to turn up at all without offering at
least some shadow of an explanation.

"Probably something about the phone," said Antonia,
looking Doris straight in the eye. "Probably isn't ringing
at their end, something like that."

"Yes, there's been a lot of that lately," said Doris,
looking Antonia straight in the eye. "Lots of people have
been having trouble with their phones."

The neighborhood was quiet at this time of day, with
only the preschool children and their mothers at home, and
they all seemed to be indoors eating lunch. The Randolphs'
house was no more deserted looking than the others, but
its curtains were still closed as if the occupants had forgotten to get up that morning. Gillian might have gone out
to shop, of course, but Win—what on earth could have
induced him just to dump those two classes without a
word of explanation?

When she rang the doorbell there was no response.
She waited a minute and tried again, with the same result.
Concluding that they had indeed gone out, she was about
to turn away when she noticed that the inner door was not
closed but standing ajar about two inches. Funny, she
thought, they're both so compulsive about things like that.
She opened the screen door and was about to pull the
inner one shut when on an impulse she pushed it open
instead and peered into the living room. With the curtains
drawn, the interior was so dark that at first she could see
nothing except the dim outlines of the larger pieces of
furniture.

"Gillian! Win!" Her voice was startlingly loud in the
silent house. But at the sound of it there was a faint stir-

ring in a large armchair that faced the door. Uncertainly, she said "Win?" again and stepped into the room, groping for a light switch.

A lamp went on beside the armchair, and the man huddled in it winced away from the light and covered his eyes with both hands.

"Antonia? Is that you?" Win's voice was almost a croak and his face, when he finally lowered his hands, looked ten years older than that of the man she had talked to less than twenty-four hours earlier. His eyes, which were avoiding hers, had a dull staring quality that frightened her.

"Win, what on earth's the matter with you?" She tried not to sound as disturbed as she felt.

"I'm . . ." He cleared his throat and his voice became almost normal. "I'm all right. It's . . . oh, my God." Once more he buried his face in his hands. Involuntarily Antonia glanced at the staircase that ran up one side of the living room.

"Gillian?" she said in a very low voice. There was a barely perceptible movement of Win's head.

Antonia's life had not been crammed with physical dangers or violence. Like most of her peers she had had a comparatively sheltered and secure existence. Yet there had been a few, a very few occasions when death had brushed past her, and each time her reaction had been the same. An overturned boat at the lake one summer. A car that flipped over on a snowy highway and left her hanging upside down by her seat belt in the wreckage. The mountain on which she got lost as a child, wandering for six hours among snowfields two thousand feet above timberline. And every time she had responded, as she did now, with an odd sort of emotional coldness. No hysterics, no heroics. Just a cool, numb efficiency that was almost robot-like. She swam to the shore, she crawled out of the wreck, she walked down off the mountain. She was neither especially courageous nor especially quick-witted in an emergency. In fact, her mind worked, if anything, more slowly than usual. But it worked. It was as if a switch marked Emotions had been thrown to the Off position and left there until the crisis was past. It was the only way she knew of surviving the few moments of real terror that had come her way.

And so it was now. The switch clicked off, a kind of deadly calm settled over her, and she turned toward the stairs. Win protested feebly from his armchair but she ignored him. She was setting one foot methodically before the other, climbing the stairs. They seemed very steep, and her feet very heavy.

When the stairs finally came to an end she found herself facing Gillian's bedroom door, which stood a few inches open. Still at the same deliberate pace, neither fast nor slow, Antonia walked to the door, pushed it open, and switched on the light. Without pausing on the threshold she walked to the bed and looked down at her friend.

The most disturbing feature of the scene was its utter normalcy and peacefulness. Everything in the room seemed to be in its usual place. Gillian's clothing was not even disarranged, and her features were composed. The masses of dark mahogany hair were coiled as gracefully as ever around her head. The small cylinder of transparent plastic that lay on the bedspread beside her looked innocuous and ordinary.

Antonia had intended to feel for a pulse or a heartbeat, but she found that even through the protective numbness that enveloped her she could not bring herself to touch Gillian's body. It seemed a superfluous gesture anyway.

On a small table next to the bed, on the side away from Gillian, there was a white princess telephone. Antonia picked it up, dialed, and waited for what seemed a long time before someone answered. When she finally spoke, her voice was clear and steady but the words came very slowly.

"I want to report a suicide. . . ."

13

Mystery of the Lost Consonant

"WHEN I WENT BACK DOWNSTAIRS WIN WAS PACING aimlessly back and forth the length of the living room. I took him out on the front porch to wait for the police. I don't think either of us could have stood the atmosphere in that house much longer."

Antonia took a rather intemperate gulp of Barry's Scotch.

"We just sat there on the front steps until the police came. I don't think we said much, either of us. When the cops got there, I told them what I could, which wasn't much, but Win"—Antonia shook her head grimly—"Win was in no condition to talk to anyone. And then when they —they carried Gillian's bod . . . body down the—oh, Barry, it was horrible!"

Greenfield, fearing she might be about to cry, hastily thrust her drink back into her hand, but this time she didn't taste it.

"I keep thinking there must have been something I could have done that I didn't. Some way I could have showed that I cared about *her* even though I couldn't take her suspicions and accusations seriously. I *knew* she was upset, Barry, that's the worst of it, I *knew* she was overwrought about the Ariadne business, and I just didn't take it seriously enough. I thought Win was just being melodramatic, refusing to leave her alone in the house like that. And I thought Gillian was only trying to inject a little excitement into her rather empty existence." Antonia shivered and glanced down at the drink in her hand as if she had only just noticed it.

"It's terrifying," she said slowly, "how little we really know about people we think we're close to."

Greenfield was spared the effort of responding to this gloomy truism by the arrival of Marsha. They had been expecting her home from her student-teaching job for the better part of an hour. She burst in now, breathless and excited.

"Oh, Barry, have you heard? They're saying that the wife of that Classics professor . . ." She caught sight of Antonia and stopped short.

"I didn't know you were here, Miss Nielsen," she said quietly. "I'm so sorry. They must be friends of yours."

Antonia nodded. "I gather," she said with some bitterness, "it's all over campus already."

"Yes, I'm afraid it is. I stopped at the English department to leave a paper with one of my professors on the way home from school, and everyone was talking about Mrs. Randolph. But the craziest thing is the *reason* they say she killed her. . . ."

"Marsha," Barry interrupted hastily, "wouldn't you like to get yourself a drink? Antonia and I are having Scotch." And gently but firmly he began to shepherd her, still wearing her coat, toward the kitchen.

But Antonia was not to be put off so easily. "Wait a minute," she said. "What did you start to say, Marsha?"

Barry shrugged his shoulders resignedly and started for the kitchen alone, muttering, "All right, *I'll* get your drink and you can extract your foot from your mouth by your-self."

Marsha continued reluctantly, "They're saying—it's idiotic of course—but they're saying Mrs. Randolph was insanely jealous of one of her husband's graduate students. I was startled because I used to room with the girl, and I know how ridiculous the idea is. But that's what they're saying anyhow."

Antonia was glaring angrily at no one in particular— the impersonal "they" of Marsha's remarks, presumably— when Barry returned with three fresh drinks on a tray. He set them down, handed one to each of the women, and put an arm around Marsha's shoulders while sipping his own highball with his free hand.

"Ariadne is a friend of Antonia's, Marsha," he said. "No one has seen her for several days, and Antonia's been concerned about her."

"Oh, I *am* sorry, Miss Nielsen, I didn't realize. But surely that part of it doesn't really bother you, does it? I mean, it's such a stupid rumor. I don't know Professor Randolph but I do know Ariadne, and it's just impossible."

"Yes, of course it is. But that doesn't prevent it from being the reason Gillian killed herself. She was obsessed with the idea that there was something between Ariadne and her husband. But what bothers me is the thought of Ariadne having to face all this when she comes back."

"Not to mention," Barry put in, "that it must be pretty awful for Randolph himself—or will be when he hears the rumors."

"Yes, I suppose so. Except that in a sense he's been asking for it for years, cultivating that ridiculous Lothario image of his so assiduously. The horrible irony of it is, now that we've been forced to take it seriously at last, the scandal has attached itself to an innocent woman."

Barry said, "Isn't it a bit morbid, dwelling on it like this? Unless there's something we can do for Win."

"I don't think there is, no. When I finally left the house, the Sandlers had come to spend the evening with him. I was afraid I was going to lose my grip before long if I didn't get out of there. And we've covered his classes, one way and another, for the next couple of days. So I can't see that there's much more we can do, not tonight anyway." Antonia leaned back wearily into the masses of soft cushions that Barry, with unprecedented solicitude, had placed behind her back when she first arrived and collapsed onto his sofa.

"At any rate, you've done more than *your* share, old girl. Tower of strength and all that." Unaccustomed as Barry and Antonia were to the exchange of compliments, they both looked slightly embarrassed at his last words.

"Thanks, but could we talk about something else? Something utterly dull and ordinary? I cannot . . . *cannot* think about the Randolphs anymore for a while." On the last words Antonia's voice rose several tones and quavered slightly.

Marsha broke in with a soothingly practical suggestion.

"Look, Barry," she said, "I'll get dinner tonight and meanwhile you fix us all another drink. You'll stay, won't you, Miss Nielsen?" It sounded more like an order than an invitation, and Antonia made a grateful noise from the depths of her cushions.

From the door of the kitchen, where he was mixing her a very weak Scotch, Barry kept a watchful eye on Antonia. She seemed, he decided, allowing for grief and fatigue, to be holding up pretty well.

When he once more returned to the living room bearing drinks, there was a dark blue book wedged under his left arm. With choreographic precision he set the right-hand drink in front of Antonia, extracted the book with the hand thus freed, set the second drink beside the first, and opened the book.

"Since you specifically suggested changing the subject, there *is* something I've been meaning to ask you about. It's my Greek." And he began to thumb earnestly through the dark blue book.

For the first time in many hours Antonia smiled, albeit a bit wanly.

"Barry's Greek" was something of an ongoing joke among his colleagues in English and Classics. Like many another literary scholar, Barry Greenfield had belatedly decided that for the true understanding of English literature it was essential to return *ad fontes*—to learn, that is, a good deal more about the Greek and Latin classics than he had picked up in two years of high school Latin and one undergraduate mythology course. He therefore badgered Antonia for several weeks until in self-defense she gave him the name of a Greek grammar "suitable," as Barry put it, "for autodidacts."

His own specialty was Henry Fielding and his theory of the comic epic. Knowing this, Antonia had put him on to a Greek text that approached the language through Homer, Fielding's great exemplar, rather than the more traditional Plato and Xenophon. Delighted with this method, Barry had plunged in and mastered in rapid succession the alphabet, the present indicative active, and two noun declensions. Thus far his progress was sufficiently typical of the autodidact's enthusiasm.

But at the first whiff of the optative mood, the dual number, and the middle voice—perils undreamed of in the philosophy of your average English professor—Greenfield's true mettle was revealed. To the astonishment of all, Antonia not excepted, Barry kept going. The middle and the dual he took in stride, the optative left him temporarily stunned—but he kept going. Doggedly he plodded through the mined fields of second aorists and passive subjunctives and contract verbs. Through a deadly rain of enclitics and particles, *nu*'s movable and *alpha*'s privative, Barry kept going. Eventually even Antonia, though noted for her skepticism on the subject of self-taught linguists, was moved to a grudging admiration. It had begun to look as if Barry Greenfield might actually read the *Iliad* in Greek one day.

He was standing before her now, dark blue book in hand, and he was saying, "It's these crazy hexameters. I can't get 'em to scan right. Look here—already in line 7 . . ." He shoved the open book under Antonia's nose and began to read.

"*Atreïdēs-te anax andrōn* . . . *Bum* ba-ba, *Bum* ba-ba, *Bum* ba, *Bum*!"

"So?" said Antonia. "Three and a half dactyls. So what?"

"So there's a perfectly *shocking* hiatus between the fifth and sixth syllables, that's so what. And hiatus," he intoned terribly, "is Not Permitted. Except, of course, sometimes. Only this doesn't seem to be one of the times. Explain, please." And he settled back on the sofa beside her with his drink, looking expectant.

Thus appealed to, Antonia was of two minds. On the one hand, she felt a vague, guilty sense of disloyalty at turning away from the painful thought of Gillian's death. But on the other, what a relief it would be to talk shop for a while—and besides, what useful purpose would be served by further dwelling on the Randolphs' misfortunes? She had done what little she could—surely the healthier impulse now was the one that urged her to turn back to her own life for a while.

With an attempt at their usual bantering tone, Antonia began. "I gather you've never heard of the Phantom Consonant Digamma?"

"That," said Barry brightly, "sounds like an Electric Company reject. Is it anything like the Silent E From Outer Space?"

Ignoring this impertinence, Antonia continued. "In primitive Greek alphabets there was a letter that looked like a capital F but was pronounced like *w*. It was called digamma or double-g, but it got lost somewhere along the line and doesn't appear in the classical Greek alphabet, which is what you've learned. Now apparently this *w* sound was still part of the spoken language when the Homeric poems were being composed, and the rhythm of the verse sometimes reflects this. In other words . . ."

"Look, Perfesser," Barry drawled, "just show me how to make that verse scan, wouldja?"

"Oh, very well," said Antonia with the testiness of the pedagogue whose lecture has been interrupted in midflight. "That phrase *anax andrōn*—Agamemnon's famous epithet, Lord of Men—was originally *wanax andrōn*, with a digamma. Therefore and QED, there is no real hiatus between *te* and *anax* because it's really *te wanax*."

"Unless," Barry observed, "you philological types just made up this Magical Mystery Consonant to pull old Homer's eggs out of the fire. Or is it chestnuts? Anyway, had you thought of *that*, my girl?"

"Sorry, but they've found digammas in primitive inscriptions from the islands: Thera, Crete . . ."

"Found what?" cried Barry enthusiastically. "A digamma? An actual charred-but-still-recognizable digamma, its bronze fittings all intact and . . ."

But Antonia refused to be diverted. "And in the Linear B tablets they've found the very word you're so exercised about, *wanax*. Unfortunately, in the tablets *wanax* doesn't seem to refer to anyone quite so grandiose as the Supreme Commander of the Allied Forces Against Troy. In archaic Crete a *wanax* appears to have been more on the order of a country squire or . . ."

To Barry's relief, with the philological waters rising icy about his chest, Antonia's lecture was interrupted once again, this time by Marsha's voice from the kitchen.

"Hey, could one of you erudite types possibly set the table and open a bottle of wine? This chili is just about ready, and I'm trying to put a salad together."

As he manipulated the cork out of a bottle of burgundy, Barry reflected with satisfaction that he might well go to his grave without ever finding out precisely what a *wanax* had been in second-millennium Crete. But at least he could now move on, with a perfectly clear conscience, to line eight of Book One of the *Iliad*.

It was three hours later, back in her own apartment, that Antonia remembered her promise to call Fedra Pappas. Even through the shock and disorientation of finding Gillian's body and helping Win through the first few hours of his ordeal, she had had the presence of mind to phone Caracci and postpone her interview with the half brother. But the boy's sister—Ariadne's sister—had completely slipped her mind.

In her present state of drowsiness, induced by a heavy dinner, three highballs, and a glass of wine, Antonia felt a guilty yearning to fall into bed and go right on forgetting about Fedra. But she remembered the girl's anxiety— though that, come to think of it, had been more for Ariadne than for the boy—and the implication of last night's conversation, that Fedra was on the point of accepting some responsibility for her brother. It would be a shame to discourage this impulse, which seemed to be long overdue. Better to reassure her that one had not forgotten one's promise to try to do something for the boy.

Antonia sighed, tried to feel virtuous, succeeded only in feeling exhausted, and picked up the phone.

Her apology and explanation for her failure to call earlier were quickly delivered. Fedra was grateful for Antonia's promise to talk to her brother, conventionally sympathetic over the death of Gillian.

Perhaps there had been nothing between Fedra and Win before. But Antonia suspected it wouldn't be long before he received a call of sympathy in his bereavement, of apology for losing her temper with him, of invitation to share a dinner or a drink. Because Professor Randolph was now one of those whom Fedra saw as her legitimate prey: an eligible man, a man with a future.

≈14≈

The Minotaur

THURSDAY MORNING DAWNED—OR RATHER, FAILED to dawn—cold, rainy, and hovering on the edge of snow. Last week's daffodils and forsythia blossoms were now no more than yellow stains on the muddy tracks that students had worn in the grass with their boots and bicycle tires. On tree trunks and kiosks all over campus, Aegean Gold posters flapped soggily in the wind.

The exhibition was still scheduled to open in just over two days, on Saturday afternoon. Miss Lilly and the museum staff were frantic, the police baffled and a bit defensive, and Yanni Pappas, after two days in jail, still uncommunicative. It was assumed that he had stashed the missing pieces somewhere—unless, of course (unthinkable thought), it was after all Ariadne herself who had spirited them away. But whoever had them and wherever they were, Caracci and his men were no closer to laying their hands on them than they had been six days earlier.

Antonia, trudging drearily toward her nine-thirty class, remembered wryly how she had felt while making the same trek the previous Friday. Then she had found the neatness, the orderliness, the pleasant respectability of the campus oppressive, and had felt both stimulated and unsatisfied by the vernal prettiness of blossoms and new grass and budding trees. She remembered how she had longed to go to Crete with Ariadne, to savor the island's violent contrasts of color and light and contour, its uncivilized harshness. Now—was it only six days later?—she only wished the familiar campus would go back to being tame and pretty and superficially predictable. As it was now, it only looked the way she felt, trampled and soggy. It did nothing at all to console or distract her from thoughts of a student missing, priceless works of ancient art stolen and perhaps destroyed—much less a friend dead by her own hand.

She got through the class. She got through her office hours—during which, miraculously, not a single student showed up in search of attention, sympathy, or justice. She managed a quick lunch in the Faculty Club, then returned to her office, packed up her briefcase, and started out the door. But before the automatic lock could click behind her she turned back, a thoughtful expression on her face, and stood for a minute before the floor-to-ceiling bookshelves that lined one wall of the room. Running a fingernail across the spines of the books on one of the lower shelves, she found the one she wanted, stuck it under her arm, and left the office.

She was remembering something Fedra had said. *I know what Ari'd do if she was here. . . .*

.

"Appreciate you coming down here like this, Miss Nielsen, especially under the circumstances. I'm sorry about your friend." As an expression of sympathy it was certainly brief, Antonia thought, but it sounded genuine enough.

Caracci went on, "I hope we haven't brought you down here for nothing but, I'll be frank with you, we aren't too optimistic about your chances of getting this boy to talk. The shrink's got a lot of fancy words for it but what it amounts to is, the kid's scared, he's dumb, and whatever he knows—if anything—he's bottled up inside himself and jammed the cork down good and tight."

"I may as well try anyway, Lieutenant, as long as I'm here. Besides, I promised his sister—the younger one, I mean, Fedra. She seems to be genuinely concerned about the boy, though from what I can gather it's a pretty recent development with her."

Caracci said dryly, "Yeah, well, I can understand her feelings. He's not exactly the cuddly type. As you'll see."

"He hasn't exactly had a cuddly life, Lieutenant."

"Yeah," said Caracci ambiguously, "that I can believe too. And what," he added, "might *that* be?"

Antonia glanced down at the book in her hand. "Oh, just something Fedra thought might get the conversational ball rolling."

A bushy eyebrow rose skeptically toward Caracci's receding hairline. "He doesn't strike me as the bookish type, Miss Nielsen. Still, anything's worth a try at this point, I guess, considering what we've got out of him so far—which is nothing. Well, here we are." He opened a small view hole in a metal door painted battleship gray and peered into it before turning back to Antonia. "Don't be alarmed by the size of him. He doesn't seem to have any tendency to violence, despite appearances. Problem is to get any reaction out of him. Like I said." He stepped aside to let Antonia take a look for herself.

She looked.

All this time, she suddenly realized, she had been thinking of Yanni, with sympathy, as "the boy," ignoring Bennie's and Caracci's references to his size and—yes, there was no other word for it—ugliness. She had assumed that the detective, at least, was prejudiced.

It was therefore with something of a shock that she saw that Caracci had been minimizing Yanni's weirdness, not exaggerating it.

The "boy"—actually he was about eighteen, Antonia recalled—was sitting on the cot in his cell, knees apart, hunched over, forearms on thighs, hands dangling listlessly between them. The posture made his huge shoulders look even more massive than they must have ordinarily.

In his eyes, which were motionless, was nothing but a blank hopeless stare. As Bennie had said, he seemed to be looking through everything that surrounded him, into some other, more bearable world.

He bore a disturbing though distant resemblance to the grotesque figure on the sign at the family *taverna*. Like the painted Minotaur, Yanni's head looked overlarge for his body, perhaps because of the huge mop of curly black hair that seemed to engulf his face. Though he was not noticeably darker in complexion than his sisters, Yanni's features were heavier than theirs, less sculptured. That and the hair were all that suggested his black father.

But the most disturbing thing about Yanni was something less tangible. It had something to do with his eyes, as Bennie Thompson had suggested. There was a certain lack of understanding in them, an unawareness of his surroundings—or was that only a reaction to his present surroundings? He looked—old man Pappas had been right in a way—not inhuman exactly, but imperfectly human. Of course, Antonia reflected grimly, he had been treated from infancy with very imperfect humanity. By everyone except Ariadne, at any rate.

She shook herself out of this unprofitable reverie and withdrew her eye from the little window. Pity and sympathy were easy enough from the near side of a steel door. Shut up inside the cell with him, alone, how would one's liberal sentiments hold up?

Only one way to find out.

"I guess you'd better open the door, Lieutenant." Antonia had the impression that her voice sounded a shade less calm and resolute than she could have wished.

As she swung the door open Caracci said, "I'll be right out here with Joe if you need anything." No doubt he intended the words to be reassuring.

Yanni raised his eyes to hers for a second, and Antonia thought she saw a flicker of hope in them. But it died instantly when he saw who she was—or wasn't—and he went back to staring through the floor as before.

Not knowing what else to do, Antonia sat down on the edge of the bed beside him, leaving about two feet between them.

"Hello, Yanni," she began. No reaction. "My name's Antonia." Nothing. "I'm a friend of Ariadne's." A small muscle at the corner of his mouth twitched at the sound of the name, but that was all.

"She's my student at the university," Antonia persevered. "And a very good one, you know, one of the best we've had in Greek." She opened the book in her lap. "The others all envy her the way she can read poetry aloud, the tragic choruses and so forth." She didn't add that the other graduate students also avoided Ariadne for the most part, sensing that outside the classroom and library they would have little in common with her.

Absently, as she babbled on about Ariadne, Antonia was turning the pages of the book that lay open in her lap. She saw the pictures herself only peripherally, since most of her attention was concentrated on finding fresh topics for what was obviously going to remain a monologue rather than a conversation.

But she knew, almost without looking, what the pictures were. The "Parisienne" fresco. The ivory bull-leaper. The Throne Room with its griffin murals. The relief of the young Priest-King in his feather crown. The gold and ivory Snake Goddess.

She was saying, "She'll have her doctorate finished soon, and then she can get a proper job and a nice apartment where you could . . ." Suddenly a massive shoulder touched hers, and she flinched involuntarily with surprise. She hadn't realized that Yanni had gradually been closing the gap between them. She glanced up at him now and saw the black unreadable eyes fixed intently on the book. He still seemed oblivious to Antonia herself, but at least he was looking at the pictures. Whether he had heard anything she had said was anyone's guess.

Softly she began to comment on the pictures.

"Those are the ladies of the court. They would have worn necklaces and earrings of gold, like these. (You'll have to tell the police where the rest of that jewelry is, you know—Ari would want you to.)

"And these are the little gold axes they gave the Goddess of War, like the one you found in the museum. They aren't for people, Yanni, they were meant for the goddess.

"This one looks like a queen, doesn't she? Or maybe a princess. Did you know your sister was named after a princess? Thousands of years ago the king of Crete had a daughter named Ariadne. She fell in love with a foreigner and helped him to find his way out of a sort of maze. The next part's sad, because he abandoned her and left her to die. But in the end . . ."

"*He knows that story.*"

When the deep, harsh voice finally broke its long silence, Antonia realized she had not really expected Yanni to speak, perhaps had even doubted that he *could* speak. He went on in a sort of lumbering singsong.

"She was a princess and she lived on an island and the sun was always shining and there was this beautiful palace and it had a dark basement and no one could get out and she was a princess and she helped him and when she died."

The flow stopped as abruptly as it had begun. It was not a pause for breath or thought, it was an end.

Was it perhaps a dim recollection of the adult's trick of pausing in mid-sentence when reading a familiar story to a child, so that the child can finish it for himself?

To humor him, Antonia prompted gently, "And when she died . . . ?"

Which version had Ariadne told him, she wondered. Catullus' romantic maiden on the beach, hair blown in the wind and pale feet in the ripples of incoming water, watching her lover's ship disappear over the horizon?

No, more likely the more ancient version, in which the princess was no lovesick girl but a goddess triumphant, bride of a god, her wedding chaplet translated into a starry constellation.

Yanni had fallen silent once more.

Antonia had been keeping her eyes on the book that lay open in her lap, but she turned now and looked up into his face.

His eyes were bottomless and black with pain. There were tears on the ugly cheeks, but his face was unmoving as stone. The sight was as shocking as if one had come upon a gargoyle weeping.

And looking at the stony gargoyle-face, she knew.

It was not after all vague anxiety or idle curiosity that had been driving her these last six days. It had been mortal fear, unwanted, denied, finally undeniable.

The cloak of cold, deadly efficiency settled upon her once again, shutting out horror, grief, anger, everything but the determination to find out what had happened.

She said again, less gently, "And when she died?"

At first there was no response from the mountainous body beside her. Then the hoarse singsong began again.

"He buried her like a princess like the Old Ones and she needed some things and they were right there and he took them and . . ."

"But where, Yanni, where?" She forced herself to keep her voice low-pitched and calm.

". . . gave them to her and she looked beautiful and he felt better."

"Yanni, where is Ariadne?" Again the small muscle twitched near his mouth.

"Like the Old Ones. Like the lab . . ." A note of doubt crept into his voice for the first time. ". . . laboratory?"

Antonia knew what he was trying to say, but for practical purposes her question was still unanswered.

"Yanni, we have to find your sister! Where . . ."

A look of immense cunning came into his face. "*Sometimes,*" he said slowly, as if he had not heard her, "they *rob* them and take *away* their things and then they have *nothing* and . . ." He paused as if to let the scattered pieces of his idea fall slowly into place. The thought, when finally completed, seemed to horrify him.

"No!" he roared. "*No! Don't* find Ari! *He hates that!*"

And without further warning the huge hands were around her throat. Just before she passed out, the last shreds of the cool detachment took note of the incongruous softness and smoothness of his hands. It was as if they had never worked, never been exposed to wind or sun.

Pale, hairless, soft hands, the hands of one who had lived in lightless places—they choked the light from Antonia's eyes and brain, and she lost consciousness.

⚜15⚜

The Princess Ariadne

WHEN SHE CAME AROUND, WITH A NECK THAT FELT broken and a throat that felt as if it had been worked over with a coarse rasp, Antonia had what was to be her first and last glimpse of Caracci looking chastened. The sight was, under the circumstances, no consolation.

"What . . . ," she croaked, then stopped because it hurt to talk. Caracci held up a monitory hand.

"What happened was, Sleeping Beauty finally came out of his trance and went for you. It took us a few seconds to get the door open and pull him off of you. And by that time you were—ah—unconscious. I'm afraid we underestimated that boy." Which was as close to an apology as Antonia ever got from him.

"I know you don't want to talk much," Caracci went on, "but can you tell me roughly what he said? We couldn't make much sense out of it. What was that about a laboratory, for instance?"

Antonia shook her head to spare her throat, which made her neck ache. So once again she croaked, miserably, using the fewest words possible.

"Not lab—labyrinth—remembered only first syllable—very confused—can't distinguish sister from princess in myth—lived in palace called Labyrinth—also thinking of

ancient burial chambers—underground—dark—oh God."
She buried her face for a moment in the pillow on the couch
where they had laid her in someone's office. The pain, the
despair, the objectless anger were physically nauseating.

Almost gently, Caracci said, "That's the next thing I
was going to ask—he said something about burying her,
didn't he?"

Antonia nodded, very carefully.

"And he said the place was 'like a labyrinth'?"

Another cautious nod.

"And nothing more?"

"I think—somewhere in museum—basement probably
—ask Bennie—knows—building."

"All right, it's worth a try." He stood up heavily. "You
try and get some rest and . . ."

Antonia sat bolt upright and swung her legs off the
couch. She felt dizzy and faint but stayed vertical.

"No!" she said, so forcefully that her throat felt as if
liquid fire had been poured down it. "I'm going too."

"Now, Miss Nielsen, don't be ridic . . ."

"I tell you I'm going, Lieutenant." She spoke more
quietly this time in deference to the throat, but there was
a murderous look in her eye. Caracci wondered if it was
meant for him but decided it wasn't.

Antonia slid her feet into her shoes, which had been
removed and set beside the couch. She stood up and sat
down again immediately, feeling light-headed. Doggedly she
tried again, and this time she stayed up.

"I'm ready," she said, and her look dared him to con-
tradict her. Caracci shrugged with a mixture of annoyance
and grudging admiration and opened the door.

She was vaguely aware of being driven to the museum
in a squad car, sitting in the back seat beside Caracci. The
swaying hurt her neck, but the pain was drowned in grief
and anger. She had not even realized another police car

was following them, until it turned off and Caracci said, "They're gonna pick up Thompson at his place—*if* he's there." Antonia was too exhausted to resent the insinuation.

They reached the museum just before closing time, though it seemed later because of the masses of charcoal-gray clouds that darkened the sky and the drizzling rain that somehow managed to make everything look greasy rather than cleansed. Caracci had his driver park across the street for a few minutes until the museum guard had ushered the last visitor out and was beginning to lock the main doors. Then Caracci crossed the street, spoke briefly to the guard, and came back to the car to collect Antonia.

"The museum's all clear now," he said. "No point getting a lot of people in a flap if they're going to be gone in five minutes anyway. The director's not around, but Miss Lilly is still here. She seemed like a sensible lady when I talked to her the other day, and I figure she knows the building as well as anyone, so . . ."

"But I thought Bennie—your men—"

"Yeah, we'll let him take the tour too if he gets here in time. Come on."

As they climbed the long flight of shallow steps that led up to the entrance, Caracci put his hand under her left elbow to steady her, but it wasn't really necessary. Terra firma instead of a swaying car, the cool evening air, and the rain were rapidly clearing her head.

Miss Lilly, looking weary, greeted them at the door of her office.

"I'm sorry the director's not here at the moment. As a matter of fact he's gone to a meeting at City Hall. It's about the burglary, I'm afraid. I don't suppose you have anything new for us?" She didn't sound very hopeful.

Antonia said grimly, "There isn't any burglary, Miss Lilly. There never was." Miss Lilly looked mystified.

"I suppose," Caracci cut in, "you know this building pretty well, Miss Lilly. All the nooks and crannies, I mean, not just the main rooms."

With a trace of her old pride in the intimacy of her relations with "her" museum, Miss Lilly said, "From top to bottom, Lieutenant, from Tower to Dungeon. There aren't many nooks in this old place I haven't explored at one time or another."

"*Dungeon*, Miss Lilly?"

She smiled. "That's what the students call it sometimes. It's really just a subbasement—large but unusable, alas. Some years ago when the humanities departments were so desperate for office space, I prowled all over the building hoping to find a few square feet of overlooked space where we could stash an instructor or two. When I found the Dungeon—only one ancient janitor even remembered it was there—I thought my prayers had been answered. I could have put the entire Romance Languages department in there. But it didn't work out."

"Why not?"

"Too cold. It's way underground and unheated. The average temperature down there is about forty-five degrees —it would've cost a fortune to . . ."

"Miss Lilly," Antonia interrupted gently, "would you take us there, please?" She sounded faint.

"Of course," said Miss Lilly, looking slightly bewildered, "but are you all right, dear?"

"She's had a rough afternoon, Miss Lilly," said Caracci, "and she needs to rest. Do you have a couch or . . ."

In a firmer voice, Antonia said, "No, Lieutenant, I'm going with you. As I said before."

Caracci's protests were interrupted by the arrival of his men with Bennie Thompson. The boy looked sullen and a little scared, and he glared at Antonia and Miss Lilly without speaking.

"Sorry we took so long, Lieutenant," said one of the men. "We hadda haul him outa bed. He was sleeping." His tone implied that he was bringing a highly suspicious circumstance to his superior's attention.

"Yeah, I do that once in a while," Bennie muttered resentfully. "I was gonna get up at six and—look, what the hell's going down, anyway?" But no one bothered to answer him. Antonia was too miserable to make the effort, Miss Lilly was as much in the dark as he was, and the policemen were preoccupied with the business at hand.

Miss Lilly disappeared into her office for a moment and emerged with a key, and the odd cavalcade set out. Miss Lilly took the lead, Caracci and Antonia followed her, Bennie followed behind them, and Caracci's two men brought up the rear.

They trooped first through the Main Hall, where a dozen posters were still bravely announcing the imminent opening of the Aegean Gold exhibition. The eyeless sockets of the Agamemnon Mask glared down at them as they passed.

At the rear of the hall was a small employees' staircase leading down to the main basement. On this lower level the corridors looked familiar to Antonia, but she couldn't be certain whether they were the same ones Bennie had led her through on Monday night. Halfway down one of them Miss Lilly stopped at a narrow door and turned to Bennie.

"Bennie, aren't there some flashlights in here?" Her tone was businesslike but not unfriendly. It was obvious that she, at any rate, still trusted him.

"Yes, Ma'am," said Bennie. "They're all working, too. I checked 'em just the other day. You want me to . . . ?"

"Yes, please. Four ought to be enough, I think."

Bennie rummaged on the top shelf of the storage

closet and handed the large flashlights out to her one by one. Miss Lilly issued two to the rear guard, took one herself, and gestured to Bennie to keep the last.

The march resumed as Miss Lilly explained, "The so-called Dungeon, as I recall, is lighted by two bare bulbs of about forty watts each, and I've no idea whether either of them is working. But even when they are it's extremely dim. The place was originally a furnace room, I'm told, though the furnaces are gone, and I suppose one didn't need much light to shovel coal by."

No one replied, and her voice sounded small, diminished rather than magnified by the faint echoes from the dingy corridors.

At last she turned into a side passage, darker and shorter than the others, with a door at its end marked "No Exit." She stopped in front of it, then turned to Caracci, who was just behind her. "It isn't locked, Lieutenant."

"No, Ma'am," he said grimly, "I didn't think it would be. Now if you'll excuse me . . ." Taking her flashlight he brushed unceremoniously past her and through the door. Antonia could hear his hand patting impatiently at the wall inside the door, searching for the light switch. The next moment she heard a click and saw a dim glow from beyond and below him, and he started down a narrow flight of stairs. She followed close behind.

One of the predicted bulbs was still working, the one at the far end of the long empty room. The floor seemed damp and uneven to Antonia. For a minute she wondered if it could possibly be made of beaten earth, but she decided it was probably her vestigial light-headedness and the semidarkness at the near end of the room that made it seem so. Shivering, she stumbled after Caracci and the jerking slices of light from his flashlight, only vaguely aware of the other three men and flashlights behind her.

The old furnace room was dusty but not cluttered. No doubt it had been cleared out at some remote period to avoid fire hazards.

There was only one thing, clearly not a fire hazard, they hadn't bothered to remove. It stood at the far end of the room, under the feeble bulb. As Caracci stepped a little to one side Antonia saw it.

It had been the footing for the huge furnaces that had heated the building during the first fifty years of its existence, a low concrete platform nearly eight feet long and about five feet wide.

It was a catafalque now.

Antonia stopped ten feet away from it and stood there, swaying slightly, eyes closed, willing herself not to scream or faint. She became aware now of an odor she had never smelled before and hoped she never would again. For a few head-clearing moments, with her eyes still shut, she concentrated ferociously on the details of the inlaid blade, remembered from a hundred art-book illustrations.

Only one of the lions had turned to face its pursuers, tail thrashing in fury over its golden back. The other two were fleeing toward the blade's point, silver bellies gleaming and paws outstretched in the graceful "flying gallop" position. Behind them, silhouetted against a background of blue-black niello, four tiny golden huntsmen with figure-eight shields stood poised to fling their silver javelins. They had stood so for thirty-five centuries, ever since some nameless Cretan artist had fashioned them to adorn the grave-goods of a Mycenean warlord.

Antonia opened her eyes, forced herself to look. It wasn't the original, of course, hiltless and ragged-edged, but the reproduction. And the girl who held it was no Mycenean princess, no Electra or Iphigenia sacrificed to the ambition of kings. She was wearing sneakers and faded jeans like any other college student, and her long black hair lay undressed and disorderly about her shoulders.

Yet perhaps she was after all, as she had seemed sometimes to imagine, descended from a line of kings even older and darker than those of Mycenae. Her face had shed the look of fatigue and timidity it had usually worn in life. Her expression now was serene, almost arrogant, and the long straight lips curved in the faintest suggestion of a smile, as if she had taken with her some triumphant secret.

And all around her, arranged in the thick dust that furred the concrete slab, stood her grave-goods—the golden cups and the silver jug, the engraved goblets, and the royal diadem. At her feet stood the huge pottery jar from Knossos, at her side a little tangled pile of gold jewelry. Her hands, clasped on her breast, clung to the embossed pommel of the Shaft Grave dagger. And on its brown-stained blade the golden lions and the silver hunters gleamed dimly just beyond her fingertips.

Ariadne had been found.

✤16✤

Nocturne

Afterward, the only emotion Antonia could remember feeling during the next few minutes was a desperate longing to sit down. It seemed somehow unendurable to stand there, hands at one's sides, and do nothing. Why it should be any easier to sit and do nothing she could not have said.

But there was in fact no place to sit except the dank floor, so Antonia stood. And the mixture of anguished thoughts and feelings that had washed over her were mercifully erased from conscious memory, leaving only the rueful recollection that she had yearned, most unheroically, for a chair.

With the exception of these first few shocked moments, she remembered the rest of the scene clearly enough. In front of her, Caracci and his men bent over the corpse, talking in low voices. Miss Lilly caught up with her, peered over Antonia's shoulder, and caught her breath sharply at what she saw. Bennie in turn came up behind the two women, silent and unnoticed until Antonia became vaguely aware of a muttered curse from him.

Antonia strained her ears to hear what the detectives were saying, but all she caught were disjointed phrases.

"Damnedest thing I ever . . ."

"Pulled the blade out and wiped it—the *blade* but not the *handle!*"

"Won't be any prints on that . . ."

"Piece of paper, sir."

Antonia only became aware that Bennie was gone when she heard the click of the latch on the old door at the top of the stairs, and the whisper of his sneakers and the bang of a door far away down one of the corridors in the basement above. The policemen noticed it at the same time.

"Thompson's got away, sir!" said one of them unnecessarily.

Caracci was staring at a piece of paper that he was holding gingerly by one corner. "Won't get far," he said absently. Then, turning to Miss Lilly and Antonia, "Ladies, how many words in the English language begin with the letters *FIV*, do you suppose?"

They looked at him uncomprehendingly.

"This paper was in the girl's hand, and that's what it says—*F, I, V*—and I can't make much sense of it. I thought maybe it might mean something to one of you."

"Five," said Antonia, her voice still a little hoarse. "That's the only word I can think of. Plus derivatives, of course. Fivefold, that sort of thing. But what . . . ?"

"But maybe it isn't *five* at all," said Miss Lilly. "I have an unabridged dictionary in my office upstairs—we could check."

"Yeah, we'll do that, Miss Lilly. Could be a name too, I suppose. Well," he went on heavily, "we'd better get on with it. You stay till I can get the lab people over here, Kominski. It'd be real funny if Miss Lilly's gold got stolen *now*, wouldn't it." It wasn't a question and Caracci didn't sound amused.

He took each of the women by an elbow and steered them back upstairs. Antonia didn't bother to protest this professional solicitude.

Up in Miss Lilly's office, Caracci used the telephone, the other detective disappeared on some mysterious errand, and Miss Lilly herself pored earnestly over the *fiv-* section of an unabridged dictionary, announcing from time to time that she knew it wasn't much help but she couldn't bear to sit and do nothing. In a low monotonous voice she recited *fiv-* entries like an incantation, punctuating Caracci's terse phone conversations.

Only Antonia was left without a function. So for a while she sat quietly in a chair, holding herself rigidly upright, trying not to think about anything. But try as she might she could not drive from her mind the sight of the young body on the concrete slab surrounded by all that incongruous magnificence of gold.

Ariadne had sometimes taken solace in the fanciful notion of herself as scion of the most ancient royal house in all Hellas. At the same time she had been thoroughly American in her conviction that hard work was the clew that would lead her out of the maze. If she had thought of herself as a princess, it was a princess in the tradition of Homer's Nausicaa who went down to the seashore with her serving maids to do the royal laundry.

Yes, Ariadne had worked long and hard. And then— again with good Greek precedent in legend and literature —she had had a fabulous stroke of luck, had stumbled upon a treasure as dazzling in its way as the bits of gold and silver strewn about her body now. This Ariadne, like her namesake, knew a good clew when she saw one. She had seized it without remorse or hesitation as hers, by right of blood as well as discovery, hers not to keep but to give back to the world.

The Euripides papyrus would have wiped out forever the family curse of fruitless anger, retaliation, and despair. It would have carried her once and for all out of the sad destructive Labyrinth her parents had built. And she would have taken poor Yanni with her, into a better life.

What a nice fairy tale, Antonia thought bitterly. So what went wrong with it? Some unscheduled dragon or wicked sorcerer came along and spoiled the ending.

Legends and fairy tales were supposed to have an enduring meaning, that was the trouble, and the ending of Ariadne's story didn't have any meaning at all. Not only was it sad and cruel and wasteful, it was incomprehensible as well.

Caracci's voice broke into her gloomy thoughts.

"Yeah, the Thompson kid. Bennie, yeah. I want him . . ." The voice dropped lower and Antonia made no effort to hear the rest of his words. Caracci's vendetta against Bennie Thompson, Bennie's reasons for bolting at such a moment—none of it mattered, none of it would bring Ariadne back.

Antonia rested her head on the back of the old armchair and stared up at the shadows on the ceiling.

Then there were other men in the room, a man with a camera and a bald man with a doctor's satchel. They were talking in loud voices, asking which way to go, and Caracci was asking Miss Lilly if she would mind. But Miss Lilly was bending over Antonia, shaking her shoulder gently, saying, "Come along, dear, there's a couch in the director's office. This place is getting so noisy. Come rest in there."

Antonia went with her like a child and sank with immense gratitude into the cushions and the darkness and the silence.

She was dimly conscious of muffled voices and shadowy figures moving beyond the pebbled glass of the director's old-fashioned office door. She remembered Ariadne's face, waxy and pale and oddly shrunken, on her gold-strewn concrete bier. She was aware of her own bruised throat. Then she wasn't conscious of anything at all.

When she opened her eyes, the pebbled glass was dark and there were no sounds at all. She sat up, feeling chilled and stiff, and saw that the reading lamp on the director's desk was on, though it was turned toward the wall to dim its light. She rose and felt her way through the darkness to the desk. There was a note on it, in Miss Lilly's firm, elegant handwriting:

> *Why don't you sleep here the rest of the night, dear? I'll be in early tomorrow to make coffee and then you can go on home for a real sleep.*
>
> *They've taken Ariadne away.* [Antonia felt a pang, oddly muted now, at the thought of Ariadne as a thing to be "taken away."]
>
> *I'll see you in the morning. Maybe both our heads will be clearer by then.*
>
> *Emma Lilly*

Miss Lilly's note was good advice. She should stay where she was until morning, she told herself, turning back toward the couch.

Only it was so cold. The day had been wet and blustery, more like fall than spring. And since Buildings and Grounds had finally gotten around to turning off the heat the day before, the office was chilly enough to make anyone long for a warm blanket. But there was no blanket in the office.

Antonia fumbled her way to the door and stepped into Miss Lilly's office next door.

She looked around her, her eyes gradually adjusting to the thin starlight from behind the window. There was the scratch paper next to the open Webster's Third: *five-and-ten, five-day week, fiveling, fivepence.* . . . No other words in English that began with *fiv*. She felt her head clearing slowly as she squinted at the old alarm clock on the filing cabinet. One-thirty in the morning. And no blanket, not so much as a shawl, anywhere in the office.

Antonia hugged herself to control a shiver and decided there was nothing for it but a brisk stroll back across the campus to her own bed.

She closed the door of Miss Lilly's office quietly behind her and set out in almost total darkness to find her way to the Main Exhibition Hall and the front doors. It wasn't far, and she was soon feeling her way toward the pale glass rectangles of the entrance. Within a dozen steps of the door, she almost walked head-on into the golden Mask of Agamemnon, peering at her out of an Aegean Gold poster hung from a pillar.

"Oops—good evening, Lord of Men," she murmured as she circled round the pillar. *"Kalispera, anax andrōn."* I must be a little giddy still, she thought.

She reached the nearest door, laid her hands upon the bar, and stopped. The bar didn't move. The museum was locked up, and she was locked in.

"Damn," she said aloud.

There was a car parked under a street light across the street that might be a police car. She could try banging and shouting. And make an even bigger fool of herself, she thought irritably, than she already had, passing out in Miss Lilly's office like that.

Then she thought of the little door Bennie had let her in and out of, the night of her last midnight visit to the museum. It would be locked, too. But it had looked much more old-fashioned than these steel-and-glass main portals. Perhaps it would open from the inside.

She turned back into the darkness of the museum.

Eventually she found a stuffy little corridor that somehow felt like the right one. A small, square, head-high window straight ahead of her looked very familiar. She could almost smell the damp grass outside.

Suddenly she noticed something else. On the left-hand side of the corridor, between her and the outside door, a vertical line of light revealed another door standing a couple of inches ajar, with a small dimly lit room beyond. Without thinking, she pushed the door open—and froze on the threshold.

It was a cubicle no more than ten feet square, lit by an old gooseneck lamp set on a battered desk. The only other piece of furniture in the room was a disreputable old swivel chair.

On it a long loose-jointed figure sprawled rather than sat, his feet propped up on the desk, his head lolling back, chuckling to himself in a low rich voice. It was Bennie Thompson. On the desk between his outsized feet stood something that looked rather like an ornamental doorknob with a long round shank. Except that it appeared to be made of solid gold.

Bennie looked up at Antonia with eyes that seemed to have trouble focusing, and his chuckle turned into a harsh, unsteady laugh.

" 'Lo, Professor," he said, waving a big hand vaguely in her direction. "C'min and joina party."

17

The Hottentot King

"WHAT ARE YOU DOING HERE?" ANTONIA TRIED TO make the question sound matter-of-fact. "We thought . . ."

"Yeah," Bennie grunted, "I gotta damn good idea what you thought." Suddenly he swung his feet down off the desk and his sullen air vanished and was replaced by a kind of tipsy graciousness. It was hard to tell whether he was actually as far gone as he appeared to be.

"Mattera fac' I'm jus' relaxing in my"—pause for dramatic effect and comprehensive sweep of arm—"office. 'Course it ain't quite what *you're* used to, but us black trash jus' gotta make do with whatever's left over after they get through putting in the broom closets and the bathrooms. If I was a white bitch, now, with a fancy *dee*gree like you or Miss Lilly—" He bit back the words "or Ariadne," but they hung unspoken in the air while the sullen look again replaced the mockingly cavalier one on his homely face.

Ignoring his bitter outburst, Antonia said, "Bennie, are you—are you sure you're all right?" Probably the boy was simply drunk, but she couldn't forget what Caracci had said about Bennie's former addiction—and the horrendous odds against his cure being a permanent one.

"Whaddya mean?" he said without interest, his consonants thickening once more. Then a glimmer of under-standing seemed to come to him and he gave a short bitter laugh.

"No, Ma'am," he said, "you guessed wrong again. No way I can afford *that* stuff no more, not on what they pay me around here. Sometime I get to feeling so goddam straight I can't hardly stand being in the same *room* with myself."

He reached down and hauled at the lowest drawer of the battered old desk. It came out with protesting squeaks, jerks, and a loud clanking of empty bottles. One that was only half empty he held out to Antonia, whether in demon-stration or invitation was unclear. In case it was intended as an invitation, Antonia shook her head. With a grunt Bennie withdrew the bottle, pulled the cork with his teeth, and took a long pull. Then, wiping his mouth with the back of his hand, he said, "Just like Ari, ain'tcha? She wouldn't drink with me neither." He raised the bottle to his lips again, then lowered it as he noticed the direction of Antonia's gaze.

Having reassured herself that Bennie was after all merely drunk and not stoned, Antonia had turned her attention to the gold object on the desk in front of him. She recognized it now, with sudden dismay.

It was a scepter, or the business end of one, of gold and colored enamels. It had been found in Cyprus but was attributed to Mycenean craftsmen, and was famous as the earliest known example of true cloisonné enamelwork. Since it was only about eight inches long, it had probably been attached to a wooden staff, to which it would have formed a kind of elaborate finial. It consisted of a golden rod sur-mounted by an intricately enameled orb on which two hawks were perched. They were also of gold, but their feathers were indicated by dozens of tiny cloisonné cells filled with green and white enamel.

As Antonia stared at the exquisite little object, it was suddenly engulfed by a huge hand. Startled, she glanced at Bennie's face. He was holding the scepter up, squinting bleary-eyed at it as though trying to figure out what it was. For a moment he had a crazily regal air, like some nineteenth-century cartoonist's version of a Hottentot king.

"Pretty li'l thing, ain' it?" he said dreamily. "Mus' be worth a pretty li'l pile o' bills too. Thing like that, a cat wouldn' hafta work for a whole year maybe. Git hisself some fine-looking chick with *real* class, not one o' these stuck-up bitches like—" He switched his tack abruptly. "Thing like that, lotta dudes woulda done more'n jus' take it, laying out there like that. Lotta dudes'd go outa their way, go to a whole lotta trouble t'get hold of a pretty li'l thing like this. A whole lotta trouble. *Maybe even kill somebody*, huh Professor? That's what you're thinkin', ain' it?" He glared with frightening intensity at Antonia for a moment, then shrugged off his melodramatic air and began again.

"Wasn' like that, though. Jus' laying out there for anyone to take. Jus' laying there. I could tell some o' the other stuff was missing, seem like one piece more wasn' gonna make no difference. They ever caught the cat that done it, they'd jus' figure he awready fenced this. An' if they didn' catch him—well, no sweat for ol' Bennie that way neither." He belched luxuriously, tried to take another swig from the bottle, found it empty, and dropped it back into the drawer with a crash. Then he fished up another, opened it, and took a long pull at it.

"Gave me a turn, seeing her like that again. Looked like a goddam queen 'er something, didn' she? Suited her too."

He took another long pull at the bottle.

"Yeah, she was a lot like that. Some people mighta thought she was stuck up. Kep' to herself mostly, didn' have hardly any friends. 'Less you count me, o' course." He emitted a short bitter laugh, which he promptly drowned in still another gulp of wine.

"Thing about a girl like that, she's making it, making it right straight outa wherever she come from, and she don' have a whole lotta time for people that ain't. Even people that are maybe trying but ain't getting nowhere. People like me, f'r instance.

"Specially the las' few weeks. Musta been a month since she said more'n three words in a row to me. Really ignored me, y'know? She'd jus' grunt 'uh-huh,' or nod her head in this sorta dreamy way. I hadn't of known better, I'd thought she was on something. Got so I was beginning to wonder if I was turning invisible or something. Gave me the creeps. Like talking to yourself, y'know? Well, I was getting sicka that shit, see, and then one night last week I stopped by her office and she damn near poured boilin' coffee on my hand stead of in my cup. Made me so goddam mad I—"

"Bennie," Antonia broke in grimly, "how did you really get this?"

"Told you how I got it, damn you," he snarled. "Like this, nothin' to it." And the big hand once again swallowed up the tiny hawks and their enameled orb.

"But Ariadne must have been in the workroom that night, and she would never have let you . . ."

"Wasn't *like* that, I tol' you," he muttered. Then his voice rose again in anger. "But you got it all figured . . . got it all figured out, ain't you? Everything about me, all figured out nice and neat. You're two of a kind, you and that mother Caracci. I had you and her figured different, though—just goes to show you shouldn't never trust no white bitch, don't it?" He half rose from the chair behind the old desk, and to Antonia the movement, after his bitter words, seemed like a threat. Nervously she backed away, and such were the dimensions of Bennie's minuscule "office" that she quickly found herself outside in the corridor.

Then she ran, stumbling and panicky, in what she prayed was the direction of the main entrance.

Behind her, echoing weirdly through the tangle of halls and stairwells, came Bennie's laughter, angry and mocking and hopeless.

18

Anax Andrōn

HER STEPS SLOWED AS SHE HURRIED ONCE MORE across the Main Exhibition Hall toward the rectangles of light that marked the front entrance to the museum. There were no footsteps behind hers. There had been none, from the moment she had bolted from Bennie's tiny cubicle, only the fading echoes of his laughter, far away in the bowels of the building.

She moved still more slowly as she crossed the Main Hall. She knew she should hurry on, pound on the glass doors, attract the attention of the policemen in the car across the street. Tell them what she knew, or thought she knew, about what had happened to Ariadne just one week ago in this building.

It had been two or three in the morning (as it was now), they had both been tired and irritable, the tensions between them had been accumulating for weeks. What had begun as a strictly business arrangement between two night owls had developed into a one-sided—what? She didn't think Bennie had been in love with Ariadne exactly. It was something more complicated, and potentially more explosive. It was a desire for acceptance as an equal, a desire to be admired by Ariadne as he admired her; it also involved envy and self-doubt and a lingering sense of unworthiness.

He had thought, quite simply, that Ariadne was his friend. Perhaps it was even her friendship that had kept him from—what was Caracci's word?—from falling, kept him for six difficult months out of that horrifying 80 percent who never escape the clutch of heroin.

Then gradually over the last few weeks she had withdrawn further and further into that other world of hers where she was alone with her papyrus and her dreams. And when Bennie, seven nights ago, had come along for his usual cup of coffee, Ariadne had ignored him one last fatal time, looked right through him or failed to answer some trivial question, perhaps even refused a drink he'd brought with him.

And all that gold was "just lying there."

Perhaps Ariadne had somehow gotten hold of the smaller items and laid them out around her for inspiration as she worked. It had never been clear how the gold had come to be lying around unprotected in the workroom, and it was the sort of thing one could easily imagine her doing.

Everything must have hit him at one terrible instant: temptation, a sense of friendship rejected, the inevitable suspicion that it was all somehow mixed up with race, and perhaps underneath and more painful than all the rest, the feeling that nothing he did—his gallant struggle against his addiction, his steady work at a decent job—nothing was good enough, not for Ariadne.

He had been wrong, of course, utterly wrong. But that was how it must have seemed to him, at least for the few crucial moments when Ariadne's life hung in the balance.

All this Antonia should tell the police. Or at least the simple fact that Bennie had a piece of the Aegean Gold in his possession, however and with whatever motives he had acquired it. So why was she hesitating?

She paused once more at the pillar with the Aegean Gold poster, the death mask of Agamemnon staring spectrally at her out of the darkness.

"Good evening again, my lord," she saluted the golden face sadly. And once more in words older than Homer's, "*Chairè, wanax andrōn*: Hail, Lord of . . ."

She stopped as suddenly as if the ancient king had struck her in the face, stopped appalled at what she had said, at what it meant, at the word that could not be unspoken now.

Not *anax* as in Barry's *Iliad*, but *wanax* as in the Linear B tablets. If you went back far enough—not just to classical Athens, but to Mycenae and Pylos and Cretan Knossos a thousand years before—the Greek language had had a *w* sound. And, over the centuries, various ways of writing it.

Slowly she turned away from the entrance, back into the museum.

She wondered dully what had caused her to make the connection at last. It had not come to her when Miss Lilly was chanting her meaningless litany of *fiv-* words. ("There are no other words *in English* that begin with *fiv*. . . .") She had not seen it when she had blundered into the Aegean Gold poster the first time that night and hailed the ancient lord by his Homeric title *anax* instead of *wanax*. Nor yet at the moment when Bennie had raised his stolen scepter and looked for one instant like a drunken lord from some undiscovered kingdom still underground, awaiting the spades of archaeologists as yet unborn.

Antonia never knew precisely why or at what moment the truth drifted up to the surface of her consciousness. She only knew that she had to be sure, that she could never voice her suspicion to Caracci—let alone to the nameless patrolmen in the car across the street—unless she was sure.

She threaded her way through more familiar halls now, found the stairs, and began to climb.

The staircase was not actually as steep and tightly coiled as those in medieval castles, but it was a fair imitation. With her neck still sore, her throat still rasping, and assorted dull aches throughout her body, Antonia found it a real torment to climb to the top. But climb she did, slowly and systematically, with frequent pauses for rest and breath.

As she climbed she tried again to think about nothing at all, and again she failed. She was afraid that she knew now what the tiny smile on Ariadne's dead lips had meant. She had taken it, perhaps fancifully, as an expression of triumph, of pride in achievement, of serene confidence that her life, however brief, had counted for something.

No doubt Ariadne's smile had meant all those things, she still believed that, but it meant something more too.

Forgiveness was not the Greeks' most conspicuous virtue. "To harm those who harm you" seemed to many Greeks the only natural and rational behavior, for woman or man. Achilles, Clytemnestra, Electra, Orestes, Medea, Oedipus—the list of noble vengeance takers in Greek tradition is endless.

Ariadne was smiling because she had joined that ferocious band of the unforgiving. She had lived long enough to destroy her destroyer, and few Greeks find that a bad bargain.

Was this also too fanciful an interpretation of a dead girl's smile? She didn't think so, but of course it had to have something more substantial behind it than a flash of intuition concerning three letters scrawled on a scrap of paper.

Antonia reached the top of the stairs at last. The door was unlocked.

The tower room was square and low ceilinged as she remembered it from her few previous visits. Yet something had changed too, something intangible that had nothing to do with the dimensions of the room or the arrangement of the few pieces of furniture. The narrow bed still stood against one wall, though now it looked as if it had been recently slept in and carelessly made. Two elderly armchairs still occupied one corner, sharing a floor lamp between them. It was, Antonia realized after a moment, the desk that was different.

It looked, quite simply, like a working desk, and it never had before.

Win was sitting behind it, looking haggard, unshaven, and startled. He stared at Antonia for a long moment without speaking. Then he pulled himself wearily to his feet, came around in front of the desk, and sat on the edge of it with his arms crossed over his chest in a parody of his old loose-limbed casualness. It was the posture in which he had charmed a hundred downy coeds, but now it looked more defensive than social, as if he were somehow protecting the desk. When he spoke at last it was with the same combination of fatigue and wariness.

"Well. Antonia. Unexpected pleasure and all that. Though I must say you look as fagged as I feel—are you sure you're all right? I've been up here since midnight last night, after the Sandlers left me. Couldn't seem to sleep in the house. Didn't get much sleep here either for that matter, but at least—damn it, Antonia, what *is* the matter anyway?"

"We've found her, Win." She watched his face carefully.

"Found? Found who? This is hardly the time for riddles, Antonia."

"Ariadne Pappas."

"Oh, Ariadne, yes. Good. I told you she'd turn up."

"She's dead, Win. Murdered."

"She's—good Lord! But—but where? When? I mean, it's hard to imagine why anyone . . ."

"The police will assume it was her brother, I expect. We found her lying in state in a subbasement beneath this building—surrounded by bits of Aegean Gold. The boy has admitted doing that. Giving her a proper burial, he called it. But I don't believe he killed her. I think it was precisely the shock of finding her dead that has made him lose touch with reality to the extent he has. He's coming out of it now, but for a while I think he actually was confusing himself with the Minoan aristocrats he and Ariadne used to read about in picture books when they were kids. Some form of regression, I suppose they'll call it—a hated and rejected child, taking refuge in the only time of . . ."

"Antonia, stop it, you're babbling." Win sounded calmer and less disoriented now, and his voice was like a therapeutic slap across the face. "I don't know what you're talking about, and I don't know why you've come here. I'm sorry the girl is dead, of course, but if you're looking for a shoulder to cry on I really think you might have found someone else right now."

As he spoke he uncrossed his arms from his chest and brought his hands down to rest on the edge of the desk on either side of him. The new position looked if anything even less relaxed than the old. But as his right hand swung down it flicked across some of the many papers that littered the surface of the desk, those papers that gave it the uncharacteristically busy air that had struck Antonia so forcibly when she first entered the room.

One of the papers swooped to the floor between them, landing with a strange click.

Startled at the sound, Antonia glanced down. Win had stooped swiftly to retrieve the fallen paper, but not quickly enough to prevent her recognizing it. Once again their eyes met, this time in a long painful gaze of mutual comprehension and horror. Finally Win straightened up, leaving the paper where it had fallen and resuming his posture of mock casualness before the desk.

Strictly speaking it was not paper he had knocked off the desk. It was a Plexiglas sleeve containing something that looked like a large dead leaf, except for its roughly rectangular shape and the faded spidery writing that covered it. Though Antonia had never seen it except in photostat, she was quite certain it was a folio of Ariadne's Euripides papyrus.

19

Theseus

ANTONIA STARED HYPNOTIZED AT IT FOR A LONG moment, while the throbbing in her head grew more insistent. She wondered vaguely whether Yanni had perhaps banged her head against the wall while trying to strangle her. She moved carefully toward one of the elderly armchairs and dropped into it with a moan of relief. Win followed her, but instead of sitting in the other armchair he remained standing, still between her and the desk.

"So it was you who had it," said Antonia. "Only the photostats were in Ariadne's desk. I assumed she'd put the originals away somewhere for safekeeping. You stole it from her literally as well as metaphorically. What did you intend to leave her, Win? Credit for compiling the index and checking the footnotes?"

"Don't make it out worse than it is, Antonia. I shall present Ariadne as my equal, my partner, my colleague, whatever you like. I fully intend to share the credit with her."

"*You* will share with *her*." Antonia's voice was bitter.

"It would have been to her advantage, Antonia. That's what I wanted to explain to her that night when I went to the museum. At *her* request, you will remember. But when I got there—God, what a scene! She was sitting there, with all that gold scattered around her. She said she'd learned the combination of the safe long ago, more or less by accident—she had absolutely no sense of professional ethics, Antonia—and she'd been taking the stuff out every night since it arrived, for what she called 'inspiration.' She said it helped her work, and I must admit she looked as if she'd been working hard. She was thinner, exhausted looking, almost hectic.

"She said, 'My people actually *touched* these very things, Win. Some Minoan lady wore these earrings, these rings, this diadem. They drank wine from these beautiful cups and took these knives to their graves with them. When I have them around me I feel strong, I never seem to get tired, I can work all night.' She raved on like that for quite a while. I told her she was talking nonsense, tried to get her back onto the subject of the edition.

"For weeks I'd been trying to make her see what a lot of flak she was going to get from the profession if she tried to publish the papyrus under her own name. I mean, she had no *right* to this manuscript, Antonia. Everyone would have resented her appropriating it like that, a mere graduate student. But all she would say was, 'I've done a good job with it, everyone will see that.' I told her she was underestimating the pettiness and greed of our revered profession. But she just smiled in that superior way she had.

"I began to realize it was all slipping away from me, Antonia, my last chance at real eminence in my field. If only she hadn't been so greedy, so selfish: there was plenty of glory for both of us, in a thing this big. I tried, really *tried*, to make her see reason, but she was so stubborn. Finally in frustration I grabbed that reproduction of the Lion Hunt Dagger. I never intended to harm her. I don't know what I meant to do.

"But she only drew herself up—I swear she looked about six feet tall—and said very calmly, 'My work is finished, Professor Randolph, nothing you can do will change that.' Then she muttered something in Greek. It sounded like Euripides' line about Jason being every kind of coward and no real man.

"I could see there was no reasoning with her, she was too stubborn and too arrogant. That bit from Euripides hit home too, I suppose. Anyway I must have lost control completely for a few seconds and stabbed her. I've had nightmares all week about the feel of that blade sliding into her flesh. . . . That snapped me out of that moment of temporary insanity and I just ran—left the damn knife in her body and ran. I think she was dead but I admit I didn't stop to make sure."

"But you weren't too disoriented to pick up eight folios of papyrus and take them with you."

"She was *dead*, Antonia, those eight scraps of papyrus couldn't do anything for her anymore. But yes, I did take them. Even so, I was in a sort of animal terror of being in the same room with a corpse. By next morning when I came to work I was much calmer, more or less resigned to the idea that I would be arrested. But then in the lounge they were talking about a burglary. I couldn't make sense of it at first, but eventually I gathered that some of the Aegean Gold had been stolen from the room where Ariadne's body should have been, only no one was saying anything about a body. I was baffled, of course, but I decided to keep quiet and see if she really had disappeared for good. I couldn't believe my luck, but if there was a chance of getting off scot-free—well, I intended to take that chance. Because this manuscript meant everything to me and Gillian."

"It meant everything to Ariadne too, Win. Her involvement with this papyrus was more than just a scholar's dream-of-a-lifetime come true, more even than a neurotic girl's obsession with the culture of her ancestors. It was this specific play that had such a profound appeal for her. She and her family had played out in their lives a tragedy very like the one in that papyrus, Win. Any sensitive reader finds that the story of Oedipus or Electra is his or her own story writ large. For Ariadne the parallels between her life and *The Cretans* were a little closer, that's all. And the catharsis that tragedy is supposed to give us—the sense of pain and grief and waste transmuted and transcended—that must have been correspondingly more powerful too."

"I don't know what you're talking about, Antonia." Win sounded bored.

"I've learned a good deal about Ariadne's background in the last few days, and it's a pretty grim story. Her father hated and despised her mother for what he saw as an act of unspeakable depravity. Her half brother, the offspring of that act, was hated, rejected, regarded as something less than human. The father himself underlined the similarities by calling his *taverna* The Labyrinth and nicknaming his other daughter Fedra. Ariadne somehow managed to survive all this and 'get out,' but even so, in spite of all she could do, the others might have dragged her back into that Labyrinth. But she found a clew, not a string as in the legend, but eight tattered scraps of papyrus. I dreamed about it one night, Win: Ariadne leading you and Gillian and Euripides out of—I don't know what exactly, obscurity, oblivion, despair—by means of a long ribbon of papyrus. That dream was trying to tell me something, only I didn't understand it at the time.

"Because the parallels between Ariadne and her namesake break down at this point. I wonder if she herself saw the irony of it. The maiden in the legend only used her clew to help the hero in *his* career, to get *him* safely out of the Labyrinth. But our Ariadne rewrote this part of the story. She refused to hand over her clew, insisted on keeping it for herself alone, to lead her out of her own personal

Labyrinth. To be blunt, Win, she didn't fancy you in the role of Theseus."

"Ingenious, Antonia, if not very flattering. You always did have a nimble imagination where literature was concerned. Accounts for those critical papers you're so good at, I suppose. But it all seems a bit finespun to me. My need for that manuscript was every bit as great as hers—mine and Gillian's. To us it was the difference between—between—" His voice had been gradually rising, and for a moment he seemed on the verge of hysteria. Then he paused and again seemed to pull himself together.

"You haven't hit it yet, Antonia, you don't know what it's like. What are they calling it nowadays, the midlife crisis? Most men survive it one way or another, probably I would have too. Even though I had the additional burden of a wife whose self-esteem was all bound up with my success or failure. Gillian had set her sights high, and I hadn't measured up. She blamed everything she could think of—me, the university, the sex-starved students who were supposedly draining my energies. Sometimes she'd even blame herself. But most of the time she was just quietly miserable because we weren't living in Princeton or New Haven or Cambridge.

"As I say, we probably would've muddled through all this, like most couples. But unlike most men, I was suddenly presented with a way out, a second chance to end all second chances. I didn't see it that way at first, didn't realize what was happening to me. I never dreamed of killing Ariadne, of course, and at the time it didn't even seem to me that I was injuring her professionally. She would still have had a piece of the glory, better job prospects, the articles and lecture invitations that naturally grow out of a thing like this. Only Gillian and I would've shared it all with her, that's the way I saw it."

"And the way Gillian saw it?"

"No. Gillian knew nothing about it. Oh, she sensed my excitement—what wife wouldn't after twenty years of marriage? In fact, that was probably what gave rise to her suspicion that Ariadne and I were lovers. She could tell that something important was going on between us, and not unnaturally she assumed it was sex. It wasn't, incidentally.

"She hammered at me about it all weekend, and Monday, and Tuesday when I stayed home. Finally Tuesday afternoon—shortly before you arrived, in fact—I couldn't take any more and I yelled the truth at her, I said, 'You can stop worrying about Ariadne, she isn't going to bother us anymore,' something like that. Then she started in again and eventually got the whole story out of me.

"She didn't say much after that. I tried to tell her I could publish the manuscript as my own discovery now and probably eventually it would mean the kind of job and the kind of life she'd always wanted. But she didn't seem to pay much attention. She just sat and stared and stared— not at me, not at anything. We went to bed early that night, and woke early yesterday morning—so early that I had time to go to the store for a newspaper before breakfast.

"When I got back she was—looking pretty much as you saw her, I suppose."

"But surely she can't have died of an overdose of Seconal in the few minutes you were out of the house buying a newspaper?"

"I didn't say she was dead. She was lying peacefully on the bed, not quite asleep. I think she saw or heard me come into the bedroom, but she didn't speak. After a minute or two I went downstairs and sat in the living room, thinking. Gillian was the only one who knew what I'd done. Everyone knew, or at least suspected, she'd tried to kill herself once before, and half a dozen people had seen how unstable she acted at the party Friday. They would all assume without question that she'd finally gone over the edge. Which of course she had, only not because of jealousy. No one would know how soon after she'd taken the stuff I had found her. I was perfectly safe. And the sense of *relief*, Antonia—my God! For years I'd been playing the role of devoted-husband-martyred-by-neurotic-wife. I was used to it, almost comfortable in it. But then suddenly, when she offered me the prospect of freedom—I took it. I just took what she offered me, Antonia, that's all."

Antonia heard her own voice without interest. It was dead and unfamiliar. "You sat there and waited for her to die."

"Remember what I'd been through in the last five days, Antonia. After that godawful dinner party on Friday I spent most of the weekend huddled in my house, waiting for the knock on the door. When I stepped out for a breath of air Saturday night I nearly got myself mugged. Sunday I went downtown to try to get Fedra off my back once and for all; I was beginning to think more clearly by then, and I wanted as little visible connection as possible between me and anyone named Pappas. On Monday I had classes to face, wondering all the while if my students or colleagues could tell that they were looking into the eyes of a killer. And all this time Gillian hammering at me about a nonexistent affair with a girl I knew was dead. If I had to defend myself in court—which I won't—I could plead temporary insanity, Antonia, in all good faith I could."

As the torrent of self-justification flowed over her, mostly unheard, Antonia slowly absorbed the horror of what he had done. All too easily she could imagine the details of Gillian's last hours and Win's gruesome vigil in the room below.

"You left her to die. Just as you left Ariadne to die in that workroom. Because she wasn't dead when you ran away, Win. She wasn't dead, she . . ." Antonia felt a wave of hysterical revulsion rising to overwhelm her, took a deep breath, and fought it down. Carefully and soberly she went on.

"She lived long enough to write something on a scrap of paper. It looked as if it might have come out of a wastebasket. Probably it was all she could reach. She wrote in Greek, perhaps to disguise the message in case you came back, perhaps because she was delirious and like her brother she fled back into the only world that had ever offered her much comfort. They were both so alone, those two, except for each other.

"What she wrote looked to an American detective like the letters *Fiv*. But the last words she spoke were Greek, and she was thinking in Greek when she died. The classical Greek alphabet has no *w*. But there was the old letter digamma that had dropped out of use by classical times. It represented the sound *w*, though it looked like a capital *F*. And of course Caracci mistook the Greek *n* for a *v* because it looks exactly like one. But to Ariadne those three letters were digamma, iota, nu. W, *i*, *n*."

He stooped again to retrieve the fallen sheet of papyrus and when he stood up to face her, papyrus in hand, it was as if he had heard nothing she said. For a moment he frowned at the mottled brown page as if trying to remember what it was. Then he looked straight at her and said, "You know, Antonia, what this edition still lacks is a good preliminary assessment of the *literary* qualities of the play. Just the kind of thing you do so well. You could think of it as your contribution to a sort of mem . . ."

"Oh, Win, for God's sake *don't*," she choked. The next minute she was back in the precipitous stairwell, groping her way painfully down the dark steps.

Seconds before she reached the bottom and entered the Main Hall, she heard the faint crash high above her. It was several more seconds before she realized what the breaking of a window on the top story of the Tower probably meant.

Caracci and one of his men found Antonia a few minutes later, sitting on the bottom step of the great staircase that led from the Main Hall up to the second exhibition floor. Antonia and the golden Mask of Agamemnon were staring blindly at each other across the dim hall, and tears were sliding unnoticed down her cheeks.

ℳ20ℳ

Aegean Gold

THE PHOTOGRAPHER HAD GRUMBLED MIGHTILY AT Miss Lilly's request for a three-by-four-foot blowup, to be made from a mediocre eight-by-ten portrait on something less than twenty-four hours' notice. She had had to tell him enough of the story behind this outrageous demand to fire his imagination and his cooperation.

The result was surprisingly effective. One had to stand back from it, of course, as from a pointillist painting, so that the thousands of meaningless gray dots could blur into recognizable cheeks, nose, and lips. It was only then that one saw the huge dark eyes and wide unsmiling mouth of Ariadne, brooding above the scraps of papyrus she had died for.

Her face now, at two removes from the life that swirled confusedly beneath her portrait, had taken on something of the androgynous serenity of a Phidian Athene, otherworldly yet faintly menacing. It would have to be an unimaginative thief, Antonia thought, who would try to steal those eight sheets of Plexiglas-sheathed papyrus with Ariadne's eyes upon him.

The manuscript was displayed in a simple glass case just below her picture. One page had been transcribed by the staff calligrapher in accordance with Ariadne's edition, and the whole play translated in feverish haste by the Classics chairman, Roy Sandler, who had been up most of Friday night finishing it.

They had commandeered a fourth-century marble bust of Euripides from its home in the Greco-Roman Statuary Hall, and it stood now beside the manuscript. The old man's deep-shadowed eyes gazed gloomily at the tattered sheets of papyrus, the flowing beard and moustache half-concealing what might have been a smile of mockery at the frenetic activity lavished upon a play that had been off the boards for twenty-four centuries.

Antonia shook herself out of her reverie. Odd that a girl dead for nine days and an old man dead two millennia should have so much more solidity, so much more presence, than the throngs that milled around their images. She forced herself to shift her attention from the dead to the living.

It was Saturday afternoon and the Aegean Gold exhibition had opened, on schedule and with a sensational unannounced addition. The mounting of Ariadne's discovery, in conjunction with the originally scheduled exhibits, was the triumphant result of an exhausting thirty-hour campaign organized and led by Miss Lilly. Under her redoubtable eye, from dawn Friday till shortly before the opening, nonstop, the museum staff had argued and telephoned, sketched and lettered, hammered and sawed and hoisted and shoved. The media people, caught off guard, were in conference downstairs with the museum's public relations department at this very moment, negotiating a filming and interview session to be held that night after the glittering special-preview crowd had departed. But the crowd was showing no inclination to depart just yet. It still filled the Main Hall, with the densest concentrations near the manuscript and the portrait of Ariadne. Champagne was still flowing freely, though Antonia's own glass, barely tasted, was growing warm in her hand.

Her eye fell on Bennie Thompson, resplendent in a gold-braided green uniform. His assignment was to guard the papyrus, but it was clear that his allegiance was at least as much to Ariadne's picture as to her discovery. Antonia watched as a well-dressed child of eight or nine—apparently a scion of one of the high society families that had turned out for the opening—daringly stood on tiptoe and tried to touch the lower corner of the portrait with one fingertip. Bennie was on the boy like a swooping hawk, and Antonia smiled sympathetically at the useless gesture of devotion. It would be good to feel that one could still protect Ariadne from something.

Caracci had found Bennie in his "office" just before dawn Friday, snoring drunkenly. He was still clutching the little scepter, so tightly in fact that Caracci could not wrench it out of his hand without risk of damaging it. Since it also proved impossible to wake him, the detective finally abandoned him to his alcoholic stupor, left a man to guard him, and went about the grim business of reporting Win Randolph's suicide. Four hours later, Bennie awoke, looked long and fixedly at the tiny treasure in his hand, and insisted on being taken straight to Miss Lilly's office.

He handed her the scepter without hesitation, saying, "This is yours, Miss Lilly, got separated from the rest. I'm sorry."

They had gazed at each other, according to the cop who told Antonia the story, "like they were doing some kinda telepathy or something." Finally Miss Lilly said, "Bennie, we're going to need all the help we can get around here for the next couple of days. I'm counting on you to help us."

So Bennie still had a job, and Antonia envied him for having an official function, an assigned task that concentrated his attention on something outside himself. Her own presence there in the Main Hall seemed to her utterly pointless, even a little indecent. She looked around, trying without much success to focus on something besides her own morbid thoughts.

Then she saw Ariadne's sister.

Fedra was standing beside one of the huge columns that ran the length of the hall. She looked as if she were forcing herself by an effort of will not to hide behind it. Though it had clearly been her intention to look inconspicuous, it was equally clear that the effort was a dismal failure. Her simple black dress, the French twist in which she had confined the mane of dark hair, had only succeeded in making her look more stunning than ever. She wore no jewelry, but as Antonia drew closer she saw that Fedra had applied makeup rather freely, not for adornment but to conceal the traces of weeping that were still apparent in the puffiness around her eyes and lips.

She was causing, Antonia could see, a kind of subdued sensation. The men eyed her with interest, the women with suspicion, until one by one they found out who she was— "the sister of the girl who died"—and then both sexes moved quietly away in embarrassment.

Fedra had apparently misinterpreted this neglect by the assembled academics, socialites, and museum officials. When Antonia approached her, it was Fedra who spoke first, a mixture of apology and defiance in her voice.

"Hello, Miss Nielsen. I hope it's all right, me crashing the party like this. I mean I did have an invitation from Miss Lilly, so it wasn't really crashing. But all these people . . ." She gestured around her with a sad little smile. "Anyway I hope *you* don't mind. I know this isn't exactly my scene, but coming here's about the only thing I could do that would've meant anything to her." She glanced up at her sister's picture, and her chin rose a barely perceptible fraction of an inch. "It isn't much, but it's the last thing I'll ever be able to do for her, now."

Antonia put an arm around the girl's shoulders, as much for her own consolation as for Fedra's. "Look," she said, "there's someone over here I think you ought to meet. He was a friend of Ariadne's." And they threaded their way slowly through the crowd to the other side of the hall where Bennie was standing, uncomfortably splendid in his green uniform, beside the papyrus display case.

Five minutes later, unnoticed, Antonia excused herself and left them talking together, sadly but with obvious relief, about Ariadne.

Antonia circulated morosely, speaking now and again to one of her colleagues but not feeling equal to any real conversation.

Barry Greenfield approached, and Antonia realized with a little shock that he was the only person in the hall she really wanted to see. She held out one hand to him, the other still clinging mechanically to the glass of long-dead champagne.

"If that," he said with unaccustomed gentleness, "is the same bubbly I saw you clutching forty-five minutes ago, I really think you could abandon it now with a perfectly clear conscience. You've done your duty by it, old girl." He took the glass from her, set it aside, and put his arms around her.

For a few seconds she let herself be comforted, but the effect was too insidious. She pushed him gently away and gave him an awkward and foolish little pat on the cheek.

"Another minute or two of that, my friend, and I would simply collapse at your feet. And for once that is not a joke but the literal truth. I'm afraid comfort is more than I can take right now. I have to hang tough just a little longer, till this is over. But thanks."

"Any time, old girl," he said, and for once there was no irony in his voice either. "Any time at all."

Antonia felt a hesitant hand on her arm and turned abruptly away from Barry.

"Miss Nielsen," said Fedra, "I'm just leaving now, but I wanted you to know. . . ." She paused as if in embarrassment, then made a fresh start. "I wanted to apologize for what my brother did to you. I know you understand that he wasn't responsible for what he was doing just then, but still—I'm sorry. Especially when you tried so hard to help us and all."

"How is he now? Have you talked to the doctors?"

"He's still kind of confused, but they say he'll pull out of it eventually. Especially if he's got someone he can count on like he did Ari." She paused again, and when she continued there was a new note in her voice. It sounded as if Fedra had done a lot of growing up in the last forty-eight hours, and it had left her with fewer certainties about life but more determination, even perhaps a dawning sense of pride.

"And I guess that's got to be me, Miss Nielsen. There isn't anyone else now."

"I suppose your mother. . . ."

"She's retired into her bottles. I figure we can't expect much help from her." Fedra spoke sadly but without rancor. "So I think I'll just try making my own life for a while, Miss Nielsen—for me and Yanni, I mean. That's what Ari always meant to do, and now it's what I'm going to do. Even if it takes a little longer than some of the ways I had in mind before."

Touched, Antonia put an arm around the slender young shoulders and squeezed affectionately.

"Ariadne would be proud of you, Fedra. And so am I."

"Thanks, Miss Nielsen. I have to go now—I'm supposed to talk to one of the psychiatrists at four-thirty, and it's nearly quarter past already. I won't forget you, Miss Nielsen."

When she reached the big double doors that formed the main entrance to the museum, Antonia saw her pause and turn back. For a long moment the girl stood there, gazing down the hall at her sister's portrait. It seemed to Antonia as heartfelt a farewell as any that was likely to occur at funeral or graveside.

At the thought of Ariadne's grave, Antonia's mind turned with a kind of grim relief to the next practical problem confronting her.

It had seemed at first more quixotic than practical. Antonia had put the suggestion to Miss Lilly with much misgiving, almost as a joke. But Miss Lilly had taken it seriously, had stared unseeing through Antonia's right shoulder for a full minute while she thought it through.

Then she said slowly, "I like it. I think—yes, I think we might just pull it off." And then, with the ladylike little smile that figured so prominently in the nightmares of the museum staff: "I'll have a word with Mr. Koutris if you like. And put me down for ten dollars, dear."

Thus abruptly had Antonia become treasurer of the unofficial Shaft Grave Dagger Committee. Its sole purpose was to purchase, from the National Museum in Athens, the reproduction inlaid dagger that had killed Ariadne.

And to lay it with her, like ancient grave-goods, in her coffin when she was buried.

Diffidently at first but gradually warming to the idea, Antonia began to canvass her colleagues and the graduate students who had known Ariadne. Without exception they responded generously. From Bennie came a pledge of thirty dollars, payable in three installments. Antonia hadn't the

heart to discourage so princely an offer, though she suspected it represented several lunchless weeks.

The little fund had grown, in the brief span of twenty-
four hours, to quite respectable proportions. And with it
had grown not only the certainty that they would be able
to meet the National Museum's price, but Antonia's own
belief in the rightness of the gesture.

The lovely reproduction, like its prototype, would
spend the centuries in darkness, outlasting Ariadne's flesh
and probably her bones. Eventually, no doubt, it would fall
prey like the original to grave robbers or archaeologists.
(And what on earth, wondered the professional in Antonia,
would an archaeologist in the sixth millennium A.D. make
of it?) But time could not touch it and—suddenly Antonia
saw just where the rightness lay—as Ariadne had snatched
the Euripides papyrus from oblivion, so would the golden
lions and the silver hunters carry her with them into a kind
of immortality. Her flesh, her bones, perhaps even her name
would perish. But those unknown diggers of the fifth or
sixth millennium, though undoubtedly they would puzzle
and argue and speculate over the presence of such a thing
in a twentieth-century grave, could hardly doubt that they
had here discovered the tomb of some very special person.